Andrea Jane Finney (nee Shaw) was born in 1966 in the village of Westhoughton, Bolton, Lancashire. She attended Westhoughton High School and then Bolton College and currently works in the Commercial Property Industry. Andrea is married to Nigel and has one son, Alex and a black labrador called Holly.

344 A STORY OF THE PRETORIA PIT DISASTER
Inspired by a Mother's Tale

ANDREA JANE FINNEY

peakpublish

Peakpublish
An imprint of Peak Platform
Hassop Station
Bakewell
Derbyshire
DE45 1NW

First published by Peakpublish 2009

Printed in England

A CIP catalogue record for this book is available from the
British Library

ISBN: 978-1-907219-00-9
www.peakpublish.com

Dedication

344 A story of the Pretoria Pit Disaster is dedicated to my father John Stephen Shaw who died on the 21st April 2008, who knew I was writing this book but never saw it published - your memory is carried with me always. And to the memory of my Grandad, Joseph Harper (1918 - 1979) a coal miner from Westhoughton, Lancashire, and to the 344 men and boys who lost their lives far too early in the Pretoria Pit Explosion on the morning of Wednesday 21st December 1910. Rest in peace

'Live for today, as life can be short,
Don't be put off by a negative thought.
Follow your heart, believe in yourself
Enjoy love and happiness, no need of wealth'

Sarah Harrison
(1826– 1884)
m Seth Clarkson
(1822 -1859)

|

Thomas	Joseph	Seth	**ELIZABETH**	William	John	Peter
			(1844 - 1923)			
			m John Gore			
			(1843 - 1904)			

William	Alice	Thomas	Seth	**Elizabeth Ann**	John	Sarah	Peter
(1868-1910)				(1881 - 1923)			
m Mary				m James Harper			
(d 1911)				(1875 - 1849)			

Mary	Charles	John	Peter	Thomas	**Joseph**	William	James	Elizabeth	Sarah
					(1918 - 1979)				
					m Ellen Whittaker				
					(1920 - 2003)				

Mary	**Joyce**	John
	(1940 -	
	m John Shaw	
	(1936 - 2008)	

Adrian	**Andrea Jane**
	m Nigel Finney

Introduction

2010 is the centenary of the Pretoria Pit Disaster, the third largest mining disaster in British history, when 344 men and boys lost their lives. This tragedy affected almost every family in Westhaughton, in Lancashire and resulted in the collapse of a once closely-knit community. This story, inspired by the diary of Andrea's great, great grandmother, Elizabeth Gore, tells of the tragedy and loss to people already struggling with life and covers the disaster at the pit in 1910 when Elizabeth lost her son, John Gore. Further research took Andrea into the archives of Bolton News and the reports of the incident form the last part of her book. This story is a fitting tribute for the 100th anniversary of the disaster.

Andrea has been fascinated with history since she was a child. In the 1970's she was given access to a diary belonging to her great, great grandmother, Elizabeth Gore, and never forgot reading about her hard life. In 2003 when she started to research her Family History she thought again of her great, great grandmother's life and the tragic loss of her son in the Pretoria Pit Disaster in 1910 and it was then that she decided to put it all together in a book.

The book is not about the technical workings of the Hulton Colliery (Pretoria Pit), the disaster itself or what caused the explosion, but to give an insight to the reader of the effect the explosion had on the community and surrounding towns.

Bolton News, has very kindly given Andrea permission to use extracts from the newspaper (by a reporter at the scene on the day and days after the explosion) written nearly 100 years ago.

Andrea has taken extracts of longer passages from the newspaper and not necessarily in the order in which they were printed. Some of the original text is quite difficult to read and therefore apologies are given for any inaccuracies. Andrea has also omitted any names relating to the deceased miners out of respect for their families.

Andrea is currently on the council committee at Westhoughton for the 100th Anniversary Memorial for the Disaster. A memorial within the town will be erected as a lasting tribute to these miners.

"This is one of those books where truth is stronger than fiction. We are given an intimate glimpse into the lives, loves and tragedies of a close knit northern community. Andrea has captured the taste of the time, and we have the privilege of tasting it too, Jack bait and all," said Jeni Edwards, Editor.

Chapter 1 Rags & Ribbons

Wednesday, 21st December 1910, began just like any other day. As usual at this time of year, it was a dark, damp, cold, miserable morning in Westhoughton. The smell of burning coal permeated the air, seeping through the walls of the houses in Brancker Street, Chequerbent, an area of Westhoughton near Bolton in Lancashire. Most of the families who lived in Brancker Street then had at least one member of their family down the pit as a coal miner, and now they were stirring into another working day.

The 'knocker uppers' were venturing out early on their daily morning routine. These young men, generally employed by the colliery, went about their duty wielding a long bamboo pole, capped with steel wire. Holding it tightly, it was an easy reach to the upstairs of the houses, and sharp taps on windows would ensure that the workers inside were woken at the right moment. Little time was given for these families to get ready for work. The night before their clothes had been positioned neatly over a chair in the back room of the house, close to the fire. The unpleasant stale stench of body odour lingered on these clothes, days old from the sweating bodies. It was an unbearable smell, but they knew little of personal hygiene. Laden with coal dust, covered with patches and repaired holes, and sometimes blood stained from the many injuries encountered down the pit, these clothes were little more than rags, but 'make do' was the watchword.

Chequerbent always seemed bleak over the months from October to March, especially for the miners, as many men and boys never saw daylight until their day off on a Sunday. They would arrive and leave work in these cold, damp and murky

1

conditions, knowing nothing else and accepting this as the norm. Their days were extremely long and they grafted hard: they had to provide to survive. What else could they do? They knew of no other line of work and this, just as their fathers before them, provided the pattern of daily life. They didn't look for change, but went about their duties, asking no questions.

Coal mining was a huge industry in the early 1900's and the town of Westhoughton had a good number of pits dotted around the community. The majority of the men and young boys earned their living down the pit. Coal was plentiful and accessible in the area and this showed within the growing community in Westhoughton. In 1851 four thousand people lived there but by 1910 this had risen to a figure of twelve thousand, nine hundred. Families travelled many miles from their previous homes to work in these newly opened pits. The cotton mills were also in abundance around the town, providing work for the women and the young girls: the 'pit' for the boys and men, the mill for the women and girls. Long hours and hard graft were the order of the day. This was a cycle of life, with children following in their parents' footsteps. It was a life where 'hand-me-downs' were the rule, so the youngest child lost out in the poorest of families. Clothes were handed down from the eldest to the next in line, leaving the youngest sibling waiting a long time before the garments became theirs, by which time they were no more than rags with many a patch on them. Nobody cared; no one gave a thought or a glance toward their garments of rags or those of others. The majority of families shared what they could, neighbours and friends alike, always on hand to help, happy in their own contented way.

Their lunch for the day consisted of sandwiches, made the evening before, wrapped in greaseproof paper or newspaper for the worse off. Monday lunch was always a miners' favourite, as the left-over potatoes and vegetables from the family's 'Sunday Dinner' were baked together with the rinds encouraging a crust to form around the food. It tasted so good, spread thinly onto the home baked bread. Other than that it was jam: 'Jack Bait' the miners called it.

In the evening the miners would arrive home from work to a hot meal of whatever was available that day, normally potatoes and vegetables. Broth could also be made with the leftovers of meat, a luxury to most available only when and if they could afford it, taken with home baked bread. After their evening meal, most men and boys would take off their leather boots or clogs and woollen socks and place their feet into a bowl of warm water to ease the pain of blisters which had formed on their tired, aching feet. Then, after reading the evening newspaper, and a trip outside in the cold to the 'privy', it was off to bed. "Always an early start in the morning," they would be thinking to themselves.

Once a week it was bath night for the miners, normally a Friday night after a hard week's graft. The old tin bath would emerge from the 'privy' brick house located outside in the back yard. It took a couple of hours to warm the bath up in front of the fire and then a good twenty pans full of hot water from the copper kettle were poured in to fill it. Father plunged in first, the rest of the family followed.

Wash day for the wives and mothers of these miners was normally a Monday routine. The fresh linen clothes starched and bleached white on this day had turned a pale colour of grey by the next day, nearing to black by the end of the week with the wear. As the week went on, the whites of the miner's eyes would turn a deep colour of red caused by the itching from the coal dust, sometimes becoming swollen and blackened. Their eyelashes were tinted a beautiful colour of ebony black as though they had been professionally dyed. Although underneath, their skin was as pale as a day of winter snow, it seemed to be suffocating from the coal dust that had settled into its pores. Abrasions were raised on their skin, face and hands, and their once soft shining head of hair was now laden with coal dust, coarse and matted, while there were blisters on their pale white feet caused by the friction of the cold leather shoes or clogs.

Many older miners suffered terrible pain from sciatica caused by working on their hands and knees below ground in the damp conditions. Lacking a good diet many also suffered some kind of bone deficiency, which grew worse with age.

Although the outside conditions that morning were bleak, there was a cheerful atmosphere in the air and the villagers were in quite good spirits. The cotton mills and the pits in Westhoughton were on a wind down for the Christmas period, and the mill bosses seemed chirpy and not their usual miserable selves, even not deducting any pay from members of staff if they were a minute late for work. Handmade decorations could be seen in the windows of the houses, nearly all made by the children, and small Christmas presents that had been bought or handmade lay positioned neatly beneath the Christmas trees. A special time to spend with ones loved ones was eagerly awaited and good times lay ahead for the Christmas holidays. Men and boys, and women too, were ready for this short well-earned rest.

"Soon be the holiday shutdown," one young boy shouted as he ran across the cobbles of Brancker Street. His clogs, a little too big for his feet, caused him to fall over on the kerb edging, He bumped into an elderly man whose hand clipped the top of his head for being clumsy, knocking his cap to the floor. The boy picked up his cap, laughed at the old man and skipped all the way up the street. He didn't care. Christmas would soon be here and this was by far the most important thing on his mind.

Streets echoed with the sound of men and boys shouting, "morning," as they briskly went about their business, clothed in their woollens, patched and repaired. With their flat caps and miner's lamps over their shoulders they were a familiar sight. Women scuttled too and fro, the sound of their clogs clattering on the ground, in sequence, tapping, as in dance. The men were dressed in little but rags, and the women and girls had woollen shawls draped around their heads and hugged close to their chests to keep warm inside while outside the material was often damp from the cold morning air.

Christmas was a great time of year for others too. This past week the children from the mission school, adjacent to Brancker Street, had been extremely busy in their various classrooms. On Monday and Tuesday last they had been excitedly involved in the production of mince pies and small Christmas puddings as part of their cookery lesson. To the children this was a welcome change to their normal lessons and was gratefully received. The fruits of their labour were eagerly awaited by the elderly of the village as a portion of their efforts were kept aside to distribute evenly throughout the houses close by. As they wandered around the houses with their lanterns they enjoyed the singing of Christmas Carols, and the results of their cooking were proudly distributed. At the end of their good deed, there was a small portion of Christmas fare left over to take home to show off to their mothers, and to be thoroughly enjoyed over the holiday.

The children loved their school mistress, Miss Randle. She wore the most fabulous and colourful outfits and seemed

5

immaculate in every way.   She had a pale complexion highlighted by her lightly blushed cheeks, and her smiling face radiated warmth to all those around. Her long, dark hair was a huge fascination to the children in her care, especially the girls, as she made many creations with plaits woven into various styles.   The girls looked upon her in awe, and from their expressions you could tell that they secretly wanted to look like her: she was so well groomed and spoke in such soft, sweet English.   The hopes and smiles of admiration from the girls soon diminished as they looked down upon their own bodies, each sighing individually at their once white, now grey, cotton smocks, the woollen socks, patched and repaired so many times with lines of threaded wool holding the yarn together, and the clogs upon dainty feet with many holes and tiny toes protruding through the hard leather.   Would they ever look like Miss Randle?

There was community spirit in abundance and an active social life in the village. The Stag & Griffin, the local public house, hosted many activities and was the central point and meeting place for the majority of men in the village. This huge Victorian stone building was located near to the entrance to Brancker Street, and its position conveniently on the main road meant it had a good passing trade. Those miners who could afford it passed many a shilling over the bar for ale, and it was their getaway for a short while. They talked men's talk and drank ale in their own company, winding down and relaxing after a hard days work.   Sunday was the busiest day for landlord Thomas Gore, with many of the miners enjoying a well earned drink after a hard week's work. Some men who drank heavily on a Sunday had trouble getting in to work on the Monday morning, still intoxicated from the night before. This was a constant cause of many arguments with their wives' and mothers, who were not so much concerned for their health, but the fact that they would lose a day's pay if they missed a day's work.

The small community was keen to support their local football team. This team was nicknamed 'The Midgets' by the villagers. Although most of these young boys were not very tall, hence the name, they were the quickest lads by far on any football pitch locally. Their home pitch was located adjacent to Brancker Street, situated at the far side of the railway track. The grass was neatly tended by the council and the area incorporated a large open space of land stocked with wild flowers and wooden benches to sit at one's leisure. In the summer months, the villagers would picnic, or take a stroll around the fields, or sit in the mild summer nights to watch people play tennis or the various bowling matches which took place on the neatly kept bowling green next to the football field. It provided a welcome chance for the children to escape to and run and play.

To gain a place in this football team was an achievement for many a young lad. Although they were feared for their skill by most of the other local football teams, they were also never frightened of producing a good tackle on their opponents. They were a team which many competitors found hard to beat, and they played with pride, enjoying their games immensely. The villagers and their families loved watching the games so there was a good following of spectators wherever they went. The team won many trophies and medals, the majority of which were displayed on a shelf at the Stag & Griffin. Thomas, the landlord, would polish their silver with pride.

The local Church of England, Catholic, and Methodist Churches around the area were well supported. Dressing up to attend their churches, the young girls loved nothing more than putting on their best Sunday frocks, shoes, and stockings for the day, the ones without holes. Some mothers would have a different ribbon tied into their daughter's hair each Sunday, or for the little worse off some sisters shared their ribbons making the other girls think that they each had a new one. The girls were so proud that small competitions were held in the street to see who had the nicest ribbon that day. Each girl looked pretty in their Sunday finery and their dads looked on proudly, but come Monday they were once again back at school in their usual once white cotton smocks which were nothing but patched rags, and hard worn leather clogs upon their feet.

At the front of the houses in Brancker Street was a private railway line. This line linked the two towns of Bolton and Atherton which were only a few miles apart. It was the main route used for the transportation of coal from one of the major employers in the area, the Hulton Colliery Company. The railway line ran just outside the front doors of these houses, the only things separating the railway track from the cobbled stones on the street were large wooden railway sleepers placed horizontally in the ground. Close by the back of the houses were the slag heaps from the nearby Chequerbent mine. The street was named after two Liverpool men, Richard and John Brancker, who where early directors of the Hulton Colliery. The building work on these houses started in the 1890s and by the early 1900's they were completed. Most of them looked identical from the outside as they followed the line of the long street, curving toward the end, bending in line with the railway tracks. The great attraction of living in these houses was the location, being close to the various pits around the town and well suited to many of the miners and their families.

Along this street, at number fifty-nine, lived Elizabeth Gore, now sixty-five years old. Widowed, she now lived alone in Brancker Street, close to her family and friends.

Standing by the window in the parlour, Elizabeth started the day by gathering her thoughts, thinking how her life was now easier in her retirement. Although her life had never been blessed with many luxuries, at last she could afford the little extras now and then. Her once golden strawberry blonde hair had now turned the palest colour of grey and had lost the texture of thickness and curls. Although not the tallest of women at 5ft 2in, she had still kept her figure and took much pride in her appearance, an example followed by her children. She was a popular lady, having many friends within the community and at her church, the Sacred Heart. Although sometimes sensitive, she was approachable and had a good sense of humour. She cherished her family and they in turn loved her. Her grandchildren always called her ' Nanny Gore' as she spent much time with them while their parents went off to work. She would read, play games and bake cakes with them – her grandchildren learned a lot from her. She was a wise owl and would give out good advice whether the person seeking it liked it or not. Worshipping her family, she was the 'mother hen' in any disputes, not that there were many, but she always calmed a situation whenever it arose, never taking sides – playing neutral - always.

She was so much looking forward to the seasonal gathering at Christmas, where all her kin would be together: there would be the giving and receiving of presents, and she would see her children and grandchildren. She wondered if she had got all the items on her list in preparation for the family tradition of Christmas Dinner at Nanny's, and she was left pondering what last minute preparations she had to complete.

In all, Elizabeth had six children. Her son, Thomas, was the landlord at the Stag & Griffin Public House, and lived and worked there with his wife Ester and their children. William was a coal miner at Pretoria Pit and lived with his wife Mary and children at number 105 Brancker Street. Elizabeth had two daughters, Sarah & Elizabeth Ann, both married with their own families, and living in the township of Westhoughton, while her two youngest sons, John and Peter and their families, had left England in 1907 to work in the coal mines of Pennsylvania, America. Both sons wrote regularly to their mother from America and when the young men had extra funds available they would revisit their roots at Chequerbent.

As her thoughts ran around in her head, Elizabeth gazed through her window and waved at some of the passers by, only just making them out in the muggy conditions of the dawn. It looked a bitterly cold day from what she could see. Turning her back on the window, she gazed at the fire which she had tended not long ago and smiled to herself as she could now feel its warmth on her body as it was all aglow with bright, colourful flames.

Sitting down on her favourite rocking chair nearest the fire, she gathered her thoughts once more and a warming smile came upon her face. "Christmas! What a wonderful time of year," she thought to herself, although a slight sadness fell on her face as she thought of the loved ones she had lost in her journey through life, "It does make you think and wonder about the past," she thought to herself, for so much had changed in her life, so much sadness, heartache and happiness she had found along the way, "How things have changed," she thought, "where has all that time vanished?"

Suddenly, Elizabeth sat upright in the chair, realising how much there was to do that day. One of her duties that morning was to go into the town to get flour and fruit for the cake she was to bake for Christmas. She rose quickly from the chair and went toward the door leading from the parlour, walking quickly through the hall into the kitchen. Making her way toward the oven, she picked up the brass kettle which held water that had boiled some minutes earlier and positioned it back on the hob. "I will have a cup of tea before I get dressed," she thought to herself, " I have a feeling it's going to be a busy day".

Chapter 2 The Moors at Shevington

Elizabeth's parents, Sarah and Seth Clarkson, had been childhood sweethearts, growing up together as children on the moors at Shevington, in Lancashire. The two lived in close proximity, their houses being a few hundred yards apart, set amongst the fields.

In 1842 Sarah found herself in the family way at the age of 16. Fearing the embarrassment of an illegitimate child, she moved to the nearby town of Bolton, lodging with a family in Smith Street until the baby was born. To family and friends in her home village she let it be known that she was working as a servant girl in one of the grand houses in the town. Seth, meanwhile, unbeknown to Sarah, had asked her father John for her hand in marriage, without mention of any child that might be on the way. John gave his blessing.

Without further hesitation Seth travelled to Bolton in search of his true love. Within weeks of his arrival at Smith Street they were married at Bolton Parish Church. Sarah had a difficult birth. It was a baby boy who arrived into the world prematurely. Named Seth Junior, he had little chance of survival and, within days of the birth, sadly died. Sarah and Seth both carried this secret with them for the rest of their lives. These two youngsters now faced a hard start to their married life, with only a small wage from Seth between them and no fixed abode.

There was no reason why the young couple should stay in town so within days they made the decision to return home. On leaving Bolton, the youngsters settled into married life initially lodging with Sarah's father, then they set up home together in the township of Welch Whittle on the outskirts of the moors at Shevington, near to her father John's farm. Seth found work at the local colliery of Welch Whittle a few yards from their smallholding and provided the best he could for them both. Sarah's family and friends were kept in ignorance of all these events that had taken place.

It was bitterly cold on Christmas Eve in 1844 when Elizabeth Clarkson was born at home in Welch Whittle. She was to be their only daughter, and her brothers, William, Thomas, Seth, John, Joseph and finally Peter followed in rapid succession.

In Elizabeth's early years, this increasingly large family rapidly outgrew their smallholding and extra room was needed. So the family moved to a small cottage at Back Lane in nearby Shevington Moor, which proved convenient for Seth, who found work in one of the newly opened coalmines nearby. Although only a two-up, two-down cottage, it was still extremely small for a family of nine but it seemed large to them – it was all the family could afford.

At the age of 12, the inquisitive Elizabeth started to explore life and was asking all sorts of questions. Why this? Why that? She wanted to learn so much about life. Her mother didn't mind the questions, even though sometimes she didn't know the answers.

"Back Lane? Why Back Lane?" Elizabeth would ask herself. She would answer her own questions if her mother and father were not around at the time of asking. "Because it's right at the back of Shevington Moors and a long walk over the fields to the nearest school, shop or church."

Elizabeth, quite content with the answer she had found for herself, thought this was quite amusing. Many of the streets, she observed, were named simply according to their location. Not much thought went into naming them and the most logical one would do.

Elizabeth had a wonderful relationship with her parents, she radiated love and warmth which shone through her wherever she went. Many happy years were spent at Back Lane, which was surrounded by fields and streams providing fresh air which many people in the coal-mining areas of Lancashire were denied. She loved to play outdoors, smelling the sweetness of nature, and picking the wild flowers that grew in the meadows. Sometimes she took bunches home to her mother, and their beautiful scent would linger for days as they were arranged in a small clay jug on the kitchen windowsill. Sarah appreciated her daughter's thoughtfulness, accepting her presents with pleasure. Every Thursday after school, Elizabeth would help her mother with the weekly baking of bread and cakes and during the spring and summer months, on Sundays, her father's day off work, they would all picnic together on the moors and once again Elizabeth would gather her flowers.

Mass on Sunday was a strict routine in this highly religious Catholic family. This was Elizabeth's favourite day, the one day she could dress up in her 'Sunday best', the one day when the whole family would be together. Her mother would wind sections of her daughters long, strawberry blonde hair in rags the night before, resulting in a mass of curls next morning. With her favourite bonnet of straw, interwoven with pink and blue ribbon, she felt she looked liked a princess for her attendance at church.

Indeed Seth called his only daughter 'Princess'. He was so proud of her and much appreciated her helpfulness towards her mother with the chores around the house. In return, Elizabeth adored her father, a handsome young man with thick, dark brown hair, rugged complexion, piercing blue eyes and sharp sense of humour. She was very proud to be his daughter and thought how lucky she was to have him as a father. Wherever they went, especially if it was just herself and her father, she noticed that the young women in the village would try to attract his attention. This was a little embarrassing to Seth, but Elizabeth knew he liked the attention and he would squeeze her hand a little tighter just to reassure her that he was committed to his family and to his beautiful wife, Sarah. He was the perfect gentleman.

The months quickly turned into years. Elizabeth's younger brothers started working at the local colliery half-time, but money was still scarce with the youngest sibling Peter only one year old and a family of nine to feed. The growing boys were getting stronger and taller and their little cottage soon became overcrowded. Sarah found a part-time job in the nearby farm as a milkmaid which brought in a little extra.

The family made the decision to move from the cottage to another farm holding which had just become available for rent. It was conveniently situated a little further up the road from where they were now living and was much larger. There was the prospect of plenty of land that could be turned in time to a working farm. Sarah's father, John, had been a farmer and, although now in retirement, he offered to give them a hand should they decide to move. The opportunity to acquire lodgers would also help with the rent. Within months the family had moved into their new home at Broadhurst a little hamlet on the outskirts of Wrightingon, the next village north of Shevington. As promised, Sarah's father came to live with and work for them. He had little money but had valuable knowledge and expertise with regard to running a farm. Sarah and Seth were happy to take advantage of his experience in exchange for his lodging. Elizabeth and her brothers loved their new home and the family settled in well.

Seth enjoyed a jug of ale, and his normal weekly routine would involve walking over to the Deer's Head Inn, a quaint little public house in the midst of the moors and a good twenty-minute walk from Broadhurst. On one Saturday evening, whilst standing at the bar chatting to family and friends, he heard cheers and clapping from the stable block just outside the back yard of the building. He was most curious, as would anyone be. He put his glass on the bar and turned to the landlord inquiring what the commotion was about. "Oh don't ask," said the landlord. "I'm not very happy with what goes on here on a Saturday night, but there's nothing I can do about it." "Why, what's happening?" asked Seth. "Well," the landlord explained, "since young Robinson took a bet with his colleagues down the pit a few weeks ago, saying he could beat any man at wrestling, all that lot in there have been having a bet and taking small wagers – its becoming a regular thing with folk wanting to try their luck. Young Robinson took home two shillings last week, said he was going to buy his missus a new dress. My worry is that maybe one day someone might get hurt, but if I try to stop them they'll only go and drink elsewhere. Then my takings will be down. I'm stuck right in the middle."

Seth didn't hesitate but wandered outside. He walked over towards the stable block where he saw a few lads he knew from the pit, Joe, John, Sam and Jack. "Are you having a go, Seth?", Jack shouted over to him. No, not me, I'm not fit enough, but I might make a bet or two. Who's wrestling next?" "Young William and Big John," replied Jack. "Right, I'll put a few coppers on Big John." Anxious but eager to start wrestling, these two competitors shook hands in the middle of the stable block surrounded by bales of hay on which the spectators sat. The match began.

The referee, Mr. Culshaw, barked his instructions., "First to hold your opponent's shoulders down for three seconds is the winner. No fists. No kicking. Just use your strength, lads. Good luck. Let's have a clean match." Culshaw was a kind and honest man, and knowledgeable about the sport. After all, he had once been a dab hand at wrestling himself in his younger days.

The match did not go as many predicted. Within a few seconds, young William, who weighed barely ten stone, seemed like a snake slithering through grass. Big John, weighing in at around 15 stone, was too slow for him. Young William won, and made it look so easy. It was all about technique and his quick thinking. Seth lost his wager this time, but thoughts of potential profits had already started to come into his mind. The lads who were wrestling were making nice wages out of it, sometimes more than Seth's eldest son was bringing home from working at the pit.

Over the next few weeks Seth became a regular spectator at the stable block and placed a good few winning bets. From his winnings he could afford to buy Mr Farrington's prized plump pig from his farm in town, from which he and his family would enjoy the meat it provided on Christmas Day and throughout most of the new year. Although Sarah didn't approve of what Seth was doing, she was extremely happy that a few more coppers came into the house when he won. The children were unaware of their father's activities at the Deer's Head.

One evening as Mr Culshaw sat on an old upturned tin bath in the corner of the stable, Seth along with his friend Jack strolled into the block. Culshaw nodded his head in acknowledgement to the two men. Now, are you two having a bet? Sam's wrestling but needs an opponent. Any offers lads?" Seth approached Sam, whom he knew from working in the same pit, "I'll have a go at wrestling you." The other men who had gathered around laughed. One said, "Are you out of your mind, Seth? You've no experience! It'll be a pushover for Sammy." Seth didn't listen; he was focussed on what he was going to do. He approached Mr Culshaw and said "Put my name down, I'll fight. I'm going to have a go." "Sam's an experienced lad, you know. Are you sure you want to do this? I don't want any accidents, lad." replied Culshaw. "Put me down, Mr Culshaw, otherwise you'll not get another penny from me." "Calm down, I'm only thinking of yourself lad - I can't much stop you, can I, if you've made up your mind? Go and get changed over there, and take them muddy boots off."

Seth stripped off his shirt and vest to reveal rippling muscles around his midriff. His pale skin had many cuts and bruises from his work down the pit. His prized possession, a pocket watch that had once belonged to his grandfather, was handed over to Jack. Then he took off his boots and his well-darned woollen socks. Leaving his britches on, he walked over to Sam in the middle of the block and shook his hand. Mr Culshaw started the fight. Seth won easily and took two shillings home to his family. He became a regular at the stable block on Saturday nights, earning more in the wrestling ring than he did from placing bets.

As Seth made his routine walk to the Deer's Head one evening, he looked around to see the show of daffodils appearing all around. It was a warm night for the time of year with a clear sky, the moonlight kindly lighting up the pathway on which he walked. On approaching the pub, he saw his friend Jack who was standing outside talking to a few of the lads from the pit.

"Will you put a bet on for me that I'll win this match tonight and in the quickest time yet? There should be good odds on that one. Don't tell old Culshaw - just say it's your money. I'll split the winnings sixty/forty with you when I've won." Seth said confidently. Jack agreed to his friend's request without hesitation.

Big John stepped into the makeshift hay ring and shook hands with his opponent. Seth had fought him many times and won four out of five fights. He was more heavy than skilful, but Seth knew how to handle him.

Seconds after the fight started, Big John got Seth on the ground very quickly and won the first score. Seth had to win the next two rounds in order to win his bet. Sure enough Seth was quick off the mark and got Big John in a bear hug. His next move was to be to sweep Big John's feet from under him, which would get him on the floor. But tonight Seth's plan of action would not work: Big John was out to win. He grabbed hold of Seth's hands which were locked around his waist, and stamped on Seth's feet. Seth had no choice but to let go. As he did so, Big John threw his head backwards to try to release himself from his opponent's grip. Their heads collided. Within seconds blood was gushing from Seth's nose. Big John turned around quickly, realizing that something bad had happened. Seth fell to the ground, motionless. He was out cold.

Mr Culshaw looked in sheer horror at Seth on the ground. Big John saw the result of his strength. Dropping to the floor he grabbed Seth's face in his hands. Big John no longer looked fearsome. He knelt silently at the side of Seth, horror stricken, and called. "Get help! Get help quickly! He's badly hurt. Go, lads, go. Run as fast as you can!" Jack ran towards Seth who wasn't moving. As he did so he shouted, "get Sarah! Quickly!" "He's just dazed," said one of the lads from the watching crowd. "Leave him be for a while. He'll come round." Jack didn't like the look of his friend. Blood was oozing from his nose at a faster pace than before and had started to seep from his ears. "Get the lad inside," he said. "He needs a doctor." Seth was still out cold.

Big John and Jack between them managed to drag Seth towards the top end of the stable block where it was a little warmer. He still wasn't moving, his body temperature was falling fast, his face started to turn blue. His skin was clammy to the touch and he was losing blood from his injury.

Seth died that evening on the 13th March 1859, at the age of thirty five. An inquest was held the following day at Preston, and the Coroner's verdict was, 'accidentally killed by wrestling.'

Elizabeth stepped out into the cobbled road from their small farm in Broadhurst, she could see the sun was shining at last, after the gloomy days of winter. There was no cold wind in the air as there had been for the previous three days. Although still cool, Elizabeth thought, this is the warmest day since September last. The buds on the trees around her had just started to break, and there was a lovely fresh scent lingering in the air. Such pleasant weather seemed all wrong for a funeral, she thought.

Like the rest of her family Elizabeth was dressed in traditional black mourning attire. Her favourite pink ribbon which once was attached to her straw bonnet from her younger days was now neatly placed in her hair. She looked around to see many friends and neighbours wanting to pay their last respects to her father, a man they regarded as a gentleman.

The time had now come to make one last walk with her father. She worried for her mother, Sarah, who looked extremely pale and had not eaten anything since the day of her husband's death, and had been shouting at the children all the time and all for no reason. She knew her mother was grieving deeply and wanted to hug her, talk to her, touch her face, but Sarah for now, just at this moment, was unable to care and comfort her children. Elizabeth too was full of anger: she had lost her father, her one true idol whom she worshipped and adored, and was hurting inside more than anyone could imagine. She took hold of her mother's arm and squeezed it just as her father used to do. She was seeking reassurance and longed for her mother's support. Sarah looked down at her and smiled for the first time in days. Elizabeth returned her smile.

Seth's father, Thomas, walked towards Elizabeth and her mother and entwined his arms in theirs. He kissed each one gently on the forehead and rubbed the palms of his hands over theirs. Comforted, Elizabeth looked at her grandfather. She could see a true likeness to her father, despite Thomas being a little smaller than his son, and in spite of his thinning grey hair. Elizabeth could see her father's eyes through his, and this thought brought some salve. Even at the young age of fourteen she understood the meaning of death. "People are born to die", she thought, "whether it be young, or old, it is God's way". Elizabeth could accept this although she was angry with her maker for taking her father at such a young age and in the prime of his life. What would she do without her beloved father?

The funeral cortege started to move forward, away from their home. The family walked together behind the hearse carrying the coffin of their loved one. Despite the grief of losing her father, Elizabeth could not help feeling some pride. As the cortege made its way through the streets around Broadhurst and then into the township of Wrightington, the villagers bowed their heads in respect as the funeral procession passed by. Elizabeth smiled politely to them. She felt important that day as her neighbours and her parent's friends had their eyes focussed upon them.

She collected her thoughts and looked forwards at the hearse. Two beautiful bay horses were transporting the cart on which the coffin carrying her father's body lay. "What beautiful creatures," Elizabeth thought, "Father would have been proud." She looked up at the coffin and saw the flowers she had put there, the last flowers she would ever pick for him. As she looked at her father's coffin, pain pierced through her body, her throat had become dry, and she found it hard to swallow. She looked behind her to see her brothers crying, comforted by her grandfather, John, Sarah's father. As she saw their pain, she could no longer control her own feelings and cried uncontrollably. Her mother, seeing her daughter's distress, put both her arms around her and kissed her sweetly on the top of her head. They continued to walk slowly, entwined together, behind the hearse. Elizabeth looked at her mother. Sarah's eyes were a well of tears. She too now had to let go, she had to let her pain out. Both mother and daughter cried freely as they made their way towards the burial place. Seth was laid to rest privately at the Roman Catholic Chapel in Wrightington. Sarah found it hard to come to terms with the death of her beloved husband, she never stopped grieving for his love and his presence.

In 1861 Elizabeth had formed a friendship with John Gore, a coal miner from Shevington Moor who worked at the same pit as her father once had. John spoke to Elizabeth on many occasions about possible employment for her in the seaside town of Southport, an area of Lancashire where distant relatives of his lived. He assured her they would hire her should she wish to take the position. Times were a little hard for the Clarksons. Elizabeth felt she wanted to help in supporting her family in the absence of her father. With the blessing of her mother, and the good gesture of her friend John's family, she packed her bags with what few clothes she had and left the farm at Broadhurst for Southport.

On her arrival in the town, she found sympathy and friendship working as a servant girl for Thomas and Mary Jane Cobham. She lived and worked at their small guest house in Bath Street, a respectable area of the town near the seafront. The houses were quite newly built, some early Victorian and others late Georgian. To Elizabeth they were like palaces. What would she make of life here? How different it was from what she had known. The houses even had their own bathrooms, and fine linens, drapes and carpets in every room. The Cobhams were a very well respected family in the community and well admired by the townsfolk. They made Elizabeth feel very welcome and treated her as part of the family. She got on well with Mrs Cobham especially, and the children loved her as she spent many hours playing with them. Elizabeth could barely read or write when she arrived, and the Cobham children started to teach her the basics. How grateful she was.

After a few happy months with the family, Elizabeth managed to save a small amount of money with which she opened her own bank account. The majority of her earnings she sent back to her mother at Broadhurst for the upkeep of their home. She was missing home terribly, but at the same time enjoying her new life. Once Elizabeth learned to read and write, she stayed in contact with her family on a weekly basis. She also wrote to her friend John Gore, at first these were letters of friendship, but over time they grew into missives of love.

Early 1863 was a turning point in Elizabeth's life. Mr William Park from Wrightington had become a good friend and companion to her mother after the loss of her husband. Although William knew that he could never be replaced by Sarah's beloved Seth, he thought perhaps she might grow to love him. Sarah was very fond of the man who farmed the fields adjoining her land. She enjoyed his company, but she was not in love with him. However, financial considerations and the need for a father figure for the boys swayed her and Sarah married for a second time.

The children were full of mixed emotions. They were glad for their mother but also felt some jealousy of this new manly figure around the house. They did feel that she hadperhaps forgotten their father. Sarah reassured her children that this was not the case.

"How could I forget your father, when his beautiful face is captured in each of you. Every day I look at you and see your father in your faces, and it pleases me." Every child had piercing blue eyes carried from their fathers genes, especially Elizabeth. Small portraits of Seth were in situ around the house, never to be moved out of place and flowers were placed on his grave once a month. The new man of the house accepted this. He never tried to take the place of their father but longed for their friendship. Respect for their new stepfather grew with each day.

That same year Elizabeth's friend John Gore, now aged 23, was on a full wage as a coal hewer at the colliery in Shevington. He was one of ten brothers and sisters and still lived at home with his parents. He decided it was time to fly the nest. He had no hesitation in travelling to Southport to ask Elizabeth Clarkson to marry him. She readily agreed, and later that same year, at St James Church on the border of Ormskirk, just a few minutes carriage ride from her lodgings at Bath Street, Southport, they were married. It was a small ceremony. Elizabeth's employers and now good friends, the Cobham's, acted as witnesses to their marriage. That very same day, John Gore brought the new Mrs Elizabeth Gore back to Shevington.

Elizabeth felt more settled now that she was back to her roots near the village in which she grew up near her mother, family and old friends. Everyone was pleased to see her back. The newlyweds set up home together at Pepper Lane, Standish, the next village south of Shevington Moor. From their house in Pepper Lane, one could see the houses at Broadhust, and this comforted Elizabeth. Although their new house was cold, damp, and extremely unhygienic, and it was most unpleasant having to share the privy with three other houses, it was home!

Elizabeth and John were soon blessed with children: William, Seth Junior, Alice and then Thomas. These years were blissfully happy. In the midst of happiness, came sorrow: sadly life was taken from two of her children within days in October 1874. Alice and Seth both died from scarlet fever: Alice was just eight years old and Seth aged only four. Brother and sister were laid to rest together in Standish, at St Wilfrid's Church.

Elizabeth's eyes scanned the other graves and then she looked up towards the sky and in her heart asking, "why?" The leaves seemed to fall off the trees as though shedding tears for these poor children as the two small coffins were gently lowered into the ground: brother and sister lying together, a communal grave with no memorial stone.

"I don't need a memorial stone to remember my children," Elizabeth said to her husband. "I know where they are and that is all that matters to me and my family." A small posy of dried lavender was placed on the grave.

Almost every family in the community had a child who had died before reaching their tenth birthday. That very same week another burial took place, this time one of their neighbour's children, Catherine, who was only two years old, and Elizabeth found herself at the graveyard again. Over the next few years, the burials continued with the death of her grandfathers Thomas and John, and her grandmother, Mary (unfortunately she never knew her mother Sarah's mother, who had died before she was born).

Over the next few years life was a hard struggle for the Gore Family. Elizabeth's mother developed a weakness of the heart and could not continue on the farm. Her relationship with William deteriorated as she never forgot her true love Seth. Elizabeth knew her mother had married in haste and for the wrong reasons, and she understood that now she was older and wiser and knew what true love was. The love Elizabeth had for John had never been there between her mother and stepfather, and the bonding and passion which she saw as a child from her parents was never evident. It was a relationship of companionship and friendship, but not love, not the love Sarah once had in her younger years. The farm where Elizabeth gained many childhood memories, the farm that would hold together her thoughts of her family, her happiness, her freedom as a child and her last vision of her father was no longer a place she could visit, or have tea with her mother. It was now in the hands of others.

Sarah Clarkson-Park died, aged 59, in November 1894, in the arms of her son Peter. Although her wish was to be buried alongside her beloved husband Seth at the Roman Catholic Chapel at Wrightington, this was not possible. This church was no longer active in worship or burial, so St Marie's Church in Standish was used as it was newly consecrated and the closest

Catholic church. As she was laid to rest another chapter in Elizabeth's life came to an end and the pages of her mind were turned anew.

Sarah left her entire life savings to Elizabeth and her brothers upon her death. This and the money accruing from a life insurance policy, once equally shared, eased their immediate financial burdens. There wasn't a great amount of money, but enough for Elizabeth and John to make the decision to move house. John changed employment as a miner and became a publican, taking over the tenancy of the Mount Pleasant Inn at Scholes, in Wigan. The future looked bright for the Gore family, a far cry from the small two-up, two-down cottage they had shared together at Standish. Three more children arrived, Sarah, Elizabeth Ann and John.

Their public house in Scholes soon began to feel cramped and rather on the small side with the new additions to the family. A decision was made to move to larger premises. John was still wanting to be a publican and so applied to the Brewery Committee for larger premises. He was given a choice of two, one a few miles out of town and another just down the road from where they were currently residing. The King of Prussia Inn at Wallgate, in the centre of the town of Wigan, Lancashire, would be a great opportunity. John did not hesitate to apply for tenancy of this town centre public house, a busy area for trade. Within weeks, the couple had secured the lease.

The family were to enjoy many happy times at the King of Prussia Inn and Peter, their youngest son, was born here in 1885. There were four large bedrooms within the accommodation - such luxury. At the rear of the premises was a small yard paved neatly with large York stone flags. Steps led down to the cellar where the beer was stored in barrels. Once a week the brewery man delivered the beer kegs and formed a good relationship with the younger children. If they were lucky they were allowed to ride on the horse and cart to the next stop.

The children enjoyed the outdoors, managing sometimes to squeeze their slim bodies through a hole in the wall of the yard which led into the beautiful gardens of the Wigan Parish Church graveyard beyond. The church was the central point of the town, and an imposing building with its fine sandstone architecture which could be seen from the neighbouring towns. On Sundays, people in their finery would venture to the church providing a beautiful site which fascinated the children. The churchyard was a peaceful setting where one could relax and recall memories of loved ones, but once dusk fell the place became eerie. The children became scared, and didn't venture into the gardens after dark.

Over the next few years John enjoyed his role as a publican, but it did put a strain on the family, with the long hours he and Elizabeth would spend behind the bar serving customers. Their children were now getting older and he often wondered whether he should get back into mining. Back once again into a routine with his wife at home, where he could do a day's work and then come home to rest and play. New pits where opening rapidly in the nearby towns, but he also knew the dangers any mine could bring. Their elder son, William, newly married to a local girl called Mary, had already made the move to Blackrod, the next village to Westhoughton, setting up home there with his young family near to a newly opened pit. John could not help but think that it would be nice to work along side his son, or at least to live in the community to be near his children and future grandchildren. A decision had to be made.

Chapter 3 Brancker Street

Although John Gore enjoyed his role as publican at the King of Prussia Inn, it took away his leisure time. It was hard work with little time off to spend with family and the demand for his services in the bar covered seven days a week, with locals drinking until the early hours in the morning. It was not the recipe for a happy family life. In 1890 he had found a place in one of the pits owned by the Hulton Colliery Co. who owned many around the areas of Chequerbent, Hulton, & Bolton. He had now received all the details from the colliery officials regarding work times, leasing of tools, payment details, and a rent book which gave details of their new house which was to be in Brancker Street, Chequerbent, Westhoughton.

Westhoughton, known locally as Howfen, was a once small mining village in South Lancashire. The newly opened pits and cotton mills were the magnet which drew many new families to the area in search of employment. The houses, billowing smoke from their chimneys, could be seen from everywhere. The winding gear of the coal mines and the chimneys of the cotton mills towered over the landscape, and on the wind came the distant sound of young children laughing as they played their games on the street corners. In the fields around the town many cattle still grazed freely in the cool wind of the mid-autumn season. Westhoughton was changing dramatically and its population was rapidly increasing.

Arriving at the local station in Westhoughton in 1890, a ten minute ride from the town of Wigan, the Gore family unloaded their belongings from the train and stepped onto the platform, prepared for their journey on foot to their new residence.

"Should be about a thirty minute walk to Brancker Street," John said as they started along the cobbles from the station path toward the main road. This was Church Street which in turn would lead them into the village centre. The sight of St Bartholemew's church with its large tower could just be seen on the corner of the road adjoining Market Street, which was the heart of the township. John recognised the church from earlier visits to Westhoughton when applying for his new job. The cobbled stones embedded in the main road were covered with manure from the horses of the many tradesman going about their business.

On the way to their new lodgings, the family were the target of inquisitive looks from the many locals keen to know a little more about these 'foreigners'. Elizabeth smiled sweetly but nervously at them. The women, although reluctantly, smiled back at her and the men tipped their hats, a gesture which reminded her of her father.

As the family walked onward, Elizabeth's eyes were inspecting the shop windows. This was a smaller community than their last town, but adequately served with greengrocers, butchers, haberdashery, bakers, cobblers, florists, hardware, ironmongers, tobacconists, doctors, chemist, dentist, and schools. Pleased with what she saw, Elizabeth smiled to herself.

"Here we are," said John, "Brancker Street." What a sight, the family thought, as they began walking down the long bending street towards their new house.

"We are going to be happy here, our John," Elizabeth turned to her husband.

"Aye, that we are," he replied raising his hand, and smacking her bottom in his loving way. The first impression for all of them was that all the houses seemed to be identical apart from the paintwork on the windows and doors.

"Where's the end of the street?" asked Elizabeth inquiringly. "It seems to go on for miles and miles."

The family had brought little with them to their new home, the simplest of bags containing a few garments and obviously their own personal possessions. Much of the furniture they had belonged to the Brewery and would be left for the new tenants at the King of Prussia Inn. Luckily family and friends had pitched in to help with the move, giving a few items of furniture for use until they could afford their own. This furniture and other bulkier items were to follow on later, once they had settled. Elizabeth was most thankful for the charity and kind help.

As they made their way along the long cobbled street, towards number fifty nine, the family thought it quite amusing to see the white net curtains moving about in many of the windows. There were obviously a number of inquisitive souls eagerly waiting to find out more about their new neighbours. Elizabeth was pleased to see a small gathering of young girls playing in the centre of the street, skipping with an old piece of rope which they found highly entertaining. Even the older boys joined in. The family approached these children tentatively and Elizabeth tried to introduce herself to them, but to no avail. Within seconds, the children scuttled off in all directions, disappearing into the various houses.

"Never mind," John said to her, "they will soon get to know us." John was quite correct, no sooner had they put their belongings down on the stone flags in front of their new home, than the children appeared as if by magic from all directions and started to ask them questions.

"What's your name mister?" Are you going to be living in our street? My mam's called Alice" Are you going to work in the pit? I live at number twenty five".

Elizabeth quickly tried to answer all their questions. Undoubtedly the children would report back, as they had probably been told to do by their parents, and within minutes the majority of residents in the street would know who their new neighbours were, where they had come from, and why they had moved to Chequerbent.

"Gosh," said Elizabeth, "I'm glad that's over, I feel quite dizzy with all those questions. Come on lets get inside".

They found the door to number 59 left open, as had been stated in the paperwork John had received from the colliery. Before he could put his feet over the threshold into their new home, Sarah pushed passed her father and ran in."

"Gosh," she said, "its quite big!"

Elizabeth Ann, being the quieter of the two, simply followed her sister, then came her father, mother then the older boys. Elizabeth Ann turned and approached her mother in the midst of all the excitement from her brothers and sister, and calmly said to her, "Mam, I love it." Elizabeth kissed the top of her daughter's head and smiled.

The houses were quite tall, and grey and with windows that seemed relatively small compared to the size of the houses. Once inside you were met by a long hallway, which appeared to be extremely dark and narrow, hardly enough space for a person to walk down in a single file. The first door to the right was the parlour, and Elizabeth's impressions were that it seemed a little lifeless and cold, and looked quite damp with patches of black stains on the walls. The ceilings seemed extremely high, making them feel quite lost in the room.

Suddenly there came a knock on the front door.

"Hello, Mr Gore? Hello," a lady with a deep rough voice shouted, "it's Mrs Brewster from number nine, hello."

Come in Mrs Brewster we are in the parlour," John replied.

Aw, its nice to meet with you all. Welcome to Chequerbent."

John replied to her kindness with a smile, "nice to meet you too Mrs Brewster. This is my good lady wife, Elizabeth, our sons, Thomas, John and Peter, and our two lovely lasses, Sarah and Elizabeth Ann."

"Hello!" responded the children all together.

"I was going to put a fire on before you got here. I was hoping to take the chill from the air for you, but never mind, you will soon be warm enough. When do you start work Mr Gore?"

"Now, I will have none of that talk, Mrs Brewster, where I come from folk call me Jack and so must you. We're not posh folk you know. And I'm due to see one of the managers from the coal board next week to see what day he wants me to start work. Our William, our eldest lad, he's living in Blackrod, and working in one of the pits over there. He's hoping to move to Chequerbent himself, and perhaps start work at one of Hulton's pits, there's many around this area."

"Good luck to him," replied Mrs Brewster, "Right, I'll leave you to settle in. If you want anything, just send one of the children up. Rent will be due next Friday, Jack, and then fortnightly after. Is that OK?"

"It is, Mrs Brewster," replied John, "I'll make sure you get it."

"Now you can either pay myself, or take it to the Hulton Offices, its up to you, either way will suit me. Welcome to Brancker Street, we are good folk up here," replied Mrs Brewster as she slowly made her way toward the front door.

"Many thanks, Mrs Brewster, see you soon."

"Aye, bye for now Jack, no doubt I will be seeing you later."

As John had said, his eldest son, William Gore, worked at Scott Pit Colliery in Blackrod, a major employer of the town, and lodged in the outskirts of the village with his wife Mary and their children. Like his father he was hoping to find work at one of the newly opened collieries in Westhoughton. Because walking was the only option and over the fields from Blackrod would take him a good hour, Mary had suggested he try to find work at the Hulton Collieries like his father and then hopefully they too could move to Brancker Street.

Within weeks the Gore family were settling into their new surroundings and home at 105 Brackner Street. William too had been granted a place of work at one of the Hulton Collieries, and soon working along with his father seemed quite normal. Hastily he made positive plans to move to the area, putting his name on the waiting list for renting. Within days he received the good news he was expecting from the colliery, and served notice to the landlord of their existing property in Blackrod. His mother and father were just a few doors up the street and of course his mother, Elizabeth, loved the idea.

Months soon passed and so too the years. The family spent many happy times at Brancker Street. Thomas, Elizabeth's second eldest son, married, and went first of all to live with his new wife's family until they could afford a home of their own. They did not have long to wait. Within months of their marriage, The Stag and Griffin Inn, located at the centre of Chequerbent village, with a main road location, came up for lease. Thomas had learned much as a child from watching his father trade as a publican and decided it would be a fantastic opportunity to go for. He attended the Brewery Offices for an interview. Although he had little experience in running his own business, the brewery allowed him a six months trial which they would review at its end. Thomas passed this trial with flying colours. The Brewery were pleased with their investment and Thomas was pleased with his new found employment. For him it was a great decision, for he was working in a trade that would support him and his new wife and future family, and the Stag and Griffin public house offered a good business opportunity.

Both of the sisters, Sarah and Elizabeth Ann, were extremely pretty and had been blessed with the most beautiful, long, dark brown hair which was either styled into a neat bun or would flow freely in the wind, shining brightly as it caught the sun's rays. Sarah, who was the taller of the two, took after her father, having a more slender frame. She had grown into a young adult and was most radiant and beautiful in every way. Her long dark auburn hair and blue eyes were envied by most of the women in the street, and certainly admired by most gentlemen in the town. She turned heads just like her grandfather Seth once had. Her courtship over many months led to marriage with a young gentleman called Charles Ord. He was new to the surroundings of Westhoughton and lived in a small cottage with his family in the Waters Nook area of town.

Elizabeth Ann, their younger daughter, carried more of her mothers genes with an hour glass figure, and although shorter than her sister she was a most attractive girl. Although more reserved and sometimes lacking the confidence of her older sibling, this did not stop her wanting to make her own way in life. When Sarah married, she felt she had lost her best friend and companion. It was now her turn to make her way in life.

She fell for the charms of an adorable bachelor and innocently, Elizabeth Ann entered into a relationship at a very early age without understanding the consequences. Within six months of courtship with the handsome young James Harper, she found herself with child. Following the pattern of her grandmother's life, James asked her father, John, for his daughter's hand in marriage with no mention of the pregnancy. With a steady wage from working in the local pit, this young couple were to set up home at Lee Common just a couple of minutes walk from Brancker Street. Their marriage took place in 1899 and the two sisters and their new husbands remained close both as neighbours and as family.

Elizabeth's youngest sons, John and Peter, were the only siblings left living at home. By 1902 both young men had followed their sisters in marriage, John marrying a girl called Mary Jones in 1901, and Peter following to marry Elizabeth Taylor shortly after.

Number 59 Brancker Street seemed quite empty in the months that followed, with just Elizabeth and John rattling around in it. But not for long, for over the next few years, Elizabeth's children were also blessed with children and the Gore family was suddenly expanding. With all the family living close by, the house once again started to fill with laughter from their young grandchildren.

On the border of Westhoughton, and its neighbouring town Atherton, was the Hulton Colliery owned by the Hulton Colliery Company, which was known locally as Pretoria Pit. The cage pulleys could be seen from every angle of the town, they seemed to be the tallest of all the pits in the area. Pretoria Pit was one of the newest pits and it was called Pretoria after the British invasion in the Boer War at Pretoria, South Africa.

Two shafts where sunk at the mine in 1900 and 1901, known as Number three and Number four. These shafts were eighteen feet in diameter and were seventy five yards apart. The shafts were split into seams in which both men and boys worked.

Locally, Pretoria was very attractive to many men and young boys as a place of work, as it had a reputation as being one of the safest in the county, and being newly sunk it had the most up to date safety measures and equipment. The majority of the men who worked at the pit had sons who had worked there from the young age of thirteen. Having large families, the mothers were only too keen to have some extra brass in their purse each week, and although the thoughts of their young children working down the mine frightened them, what else could they do? With the lack of a good education, and the majority not able to read or write properly, working at another trade was out of the question. Having left school at this young age, most of the children became slaves to the system, there was no other way to go.

Pretoria pit turned out to be an extremely prosperous and active mine, which brought incredible wealth to those who owned it. On the other hand, many miners could not afford to buy their own tools, and in turn rented them from the colliery each week. The houses in Brancker Street were also owned by the Hulton Colliery Company, and the majority of these miners, upon receiving their weekly pay packet, put aside a certain amount of shillings which of course went back to the coal company in the form of rent.

In total nearly two thousand men and boys worked at Pretoria on various shifts, the majority being from Westhoughton, the remainder from the neighbouring towns. Approximately, two thousand tons of coal was brought to the surface of the colliery every day, which equated to an average of one ton per worker per day.

John Gore and his sons, William, John and Peter all transferred from their local places of work to start work at this newly opened pit.

For Elizabeth, 1904 was a tragic and sad year. Her son Thomas lost his youngest child, Joseph, from fever in the spring. Elizabeth had seen this before and it brought back memories of losing her own two young children, Alice and Seth, from the same disease. Her daughter Sarah also lost a child in the summer months that followed, a daughter sadly still-born. And then William, her eldest, also lost a child, once again with fever, a little girl, the second child of his that had died.

In the same year, their father John was taken ill at the colliery in October. He had caught a chill on his chest and had much trouble breathing. He was advised by the doctor to rest for a couple of days and to keep warm, the concern being that he needed to be fully well to work with the cold of winter coming on. John would not accept the fact that he was ill and went back to work sooner than recommended by his doctor. Over the next couple of weeks he struggled enormously with a heavy cold and working in the cold and damp conditions of the mine. Elizabeth demanded that he rest. This time he obeyed his wife's wishes and said he would indeed rest. Over the next few days, John Gore's health deteriorated and he was confined to bed. He had huge difficulty breathing and his lungs would fill with fluid causing him immense pain, and he had started to cough up blood mixed with his phlegm. Elizabeth knew she was losing her husband and called her children to be with her. John Gore slipped away into a deep sleep on the 20th October and never regained consciousness. He died on 21st October 1904 with his family around him. Elizabeth's rock was now gone, what would she do without him?

Over the next months, with much love from the family and the utmost support from neighbours and friends, Elizabeth started to recover from her grief and slowly began to rebuild her life again. One wish of her husband was that he was to be buried with his two young children, Seth and Alice, at Standish. Elizabeth obeyed her husband's wish and thereafter made a fortnightly trip to place flowers upon the grave. Her home at Brancker Street was filled with photographs of her passed loved ones. They were with her always, she thought, as she polished the dust from their cherished photograph frames every week with pride.

Elizabeth's eldest son, William liked his drink. This was a habit not hard to satisfy as his brother Thomas was landlord of his local, known as 'The Stag' for short. One of William's other habits was that he liked to gamble. Although not blessed with many riches he did have a few shillings to spare every now and then and these he would gamble away, losing most of it, but keeping his wife, Mary, ignorant of his passtime.

Friday night was his favourite night for combining both the pleasures of liquor and gambling. Finishing work on a Friday evening and collecting his weekly pay, he knew he could relax a while as his Saturday shift down the mine was the morning only, finishing at 1pm.

Apart from a Sunday, Friday night was a regular meeting time for the majority of the men. The lads and dads from the football team would sit in the corner of the tap room and discuss their plan of attack on the opposition for the Saturday game.

Not many women ventured into the Stag and Griffin, and the one or two who did would sit in the lounge. The back room of the Stag & Griffin was known locally as the den, or another word used was the tap room, and this was a 'women free zone'. The men and lads could let their hair down in their secret sanctuary and the language which could be heard emanating from the room was often foul.

Much money passed around the tables from the various games of cards and dominoes, and even the landlord, Thomas, would join in. Afterwards, he would also have to count the cost of his many nights spent drinking and gambling round the table with his brother William and his friends as he counted his takings the next day. Pieces of paper were scattered all around the floor, and behind the bar, all being unsigned IOU's, or 'subs' as the men called them, of those who had not wanted to leave the inn when their money ran out.

These men where 'canny.' They knew that to get the landlord drunk on a night and involved in their games was easy   They also knew that Thomas, although a stern level-headed man when sober, under the influence of alcohol he would give any man anything if he had it, especially beer. The fun started the following week after their Friday night jaunts. The men in the village would avoid the inn like the plague so as not to pay the money back on their subs. Would he remember? Let's hope he forgets! The men even took wagers on this regular occurrence to see if and who would get away with it.

Meanwhile, Thomas would stand at the bar sheepishly and look around at his customers. He would try, without proof, to work out who owed him money when the men eventually went back for their regular pint on a Friday, although there were some men, the minority, who did own up to their dues and did offer payment to the landlord.   Thomas's accountant, Mr Hunter from Wigan, often wondered how he made a living as a publican. He did, of course, but only by putting his losses against spillage, and by cultivating the other regular customers who paid for their ale.

Thomas would organize annual day trips to Blackpool on the Flyde coast, north of Lancashire. These were for the men only. Women strictly not allowed. A charabanc would pick the men up outside the inn early in the morning of a weekend, around 8am for an expected arrival at their destination of around 10.30am. The men looked forward to these trips, however, their wives and girlfriends did not approve as many tales were told upon their return of flirtations with the beautifully dressed women and girls.

Chapter 4 - 21st December 1910

Wednesday morning, William Gore had been woken by the 'knocker upper' at 6.30am. Quickly he got out of bed, and although he thought about 'playing' (having a day off), he realised that there were only a couple of days to go till Christmas and the money was needed to buy the little extras for his wife and children. He was so much looking forward to the break from work. As he stood at the side of the bed, he looked at his wife Mary, still sleeping, and leaning over her shoulder planted a kiss on the top of her head. William knew she wasn't deep asleep because she slowly opened her eyes to acknowledge his gesture. Within seconds her eyes were closed again and she turned over in bed and went back to sleep. William was left struggling in the dark to find the match box left on the bedside cabinet so that he could light one of the numerous candles left lying around. As he struck the match it instantly went out. "Bugger me," he snapped under his breath, "it must be cold." The second match was lit and so too the candle. Still in his undergarments, he picked it up and made his way to the top of the stairs. As he passed, he looked into the opposite room where his children were sleeping. There were four of them in that room, William Junior, Elizabeth, Catherine (Kitty) and Seth snuggled together, while Frances and their youngest, Thomas slept in a small bed in their parent's room.

William walked slowly down the stairs, desperately trying not to wake the children as each stair creaked with his every footstep. Next he walked toward the parlour where he knew his son John was sleeping with his wife Mary. Very quietly made his way to the side of their bed and gently tapped John on the shoulder. William glanced down and thought it was a shame to waken him: although now a grown man at 23, he was still his first born, his little boy.

"John, John, come on lad, its time for work" he whispered softly.

William lit another candle which stood on a shelf near to the fire so that John could see a little better when he eventually got out of bed. William left the room and made his way to the kitchen to put the kettle on the hob to make a pot of tea. He thoroughly enjoyed his cup of tea in the morning: he would say that it set him up for the day. Mary had prepared both their lunches the night before and placed them in a two small tins with a couple of home made ginger biscuits and an apple in each. William opened the tin to find what lunch was. Cheese, his favourite!

Moving toward the clothes' maiden, he found his working gear from the day before hanging neatly over it ready for him to put on. Luckily they were still warm from the fire which was aglow from the night before. He had left his undergarments on as they acted as a thermal protector in the cold days of winter, so he quickly put on his blue striped shirt which had been bought as a Christmas present the year before last from his mother, then his woollen socks darned many times by his wife, and lastly his pit drawers, which were very badly soiled from the pit workings.

He looked down at his pit drawers and smiled to himself. His daughter Kitty was a great help to her mother with the many chores to be done around the house. He had mentioned only a couple of days before that his britches had a couple of holes which had started to appear at the knees, a common occurrence from his duty down the mine. Kitty must have heard these words and taken it upon herself to mend them. She must have used any leftover material she could find because the material and colour she had used to make the patches with was white and blue, which showed up clearly on her father britches, which were black. He didn't care that the colour of material didn't match, these britches were patched and repaired by his daughter, by her own tiny hands, and he was proud to wear them.

Once dressed, William made his way back into the parlour to make sure his son was out of bed. He wasn't, as was clear because of the silence in the room. Once again he tapped John's shoulder and told him to get a move on. John woke, acknowledged his father and made a slow attempt to get out of bed. William, seeing his son awake at last, made his way back to the kitchen to finish making the pot of tea. He sat down in the chair whilst waiting for the kettle to boil. It was now 6.15am. Father and son normally left the house at 6.30am and with a brisk walk over the fields to the pit would make it in time for the start of the working day. They normally arrived at the pit office about 6.45am.

The kettle started to whistle from the steam of the hot water now boiling inside. William snatched it quickly away from the hob so as not to disturb the rest of the family, poured the water into the teapot and let the tea brew whilst he got the milk from the larder.

William sat down with a hot mug of tea. He could not hear any movement from his son's room. "He's not out of bed, the lazy bugger!" he cursed under his breath. William got up from the chair and went back to the parlour. He opened the door and was just about to lose his temper with his son when John looked up at his father.

"Pa, I'm not feeling too good. My belly's off and I feel sick. I think I have gotten a cold as well and me head feels all muzzy. I don't think I'm going in today. If I do, pa, I'm going to be worse and I don't want to be ill over Christmas."

William looked down at John feeling a little annoyed with his son, although if he was honest, he was feeling jealous of the fact that he could go back to bed and miss a whole day down the cold dark mine. Placing his head on one side, he looked at John again and thought that he did look rather pale, and although he wouldn't admit it to himself, his fatherly feelings took over and extended sympathy toward his son.

William whispered, "right lad, you stay there, and make use of yourself in the house today, help your mother with her duties. I'll see you at tea time. Make sure you blow out that candle John if you're stopping here."

John glanced up at his father, nodded and said, "See ya!" William moved toward the door, looking back at his son: John gave a wan smile and his father responded with a nod of his head. William walked through the door and made his way to the kitchen to finish his cup of tea. He had less than five minutes to get on his way. He quickly drank the tea and put the cup into the kitchen sink. He looked at the table to see both lunch tins. Happily, he thought, I'll not be hungry today. He picked up both tins, his pipe, tobacco and matches, a few shillings and pennies and transferred them all into his brown leather work bag, which was a little shabby and well used. He glanced round the kitchen and smiled to himself. How quiet and peaceful it is he thought, but it won't be peaceful when I get home for tea that's for sure. Now there's something to look forward to after a long day down the pit, and he chuckled to himself.

It was good timing, for as he stepped out onto the street, Albert, one of William's workmates was walking briskly past no 105 and he could just make out the figure under the flickering gas lamp that lit up the street on these dark mornings,

"Morning Bill," Albert shouted.

"Morning Bert, its bloody cold this morning isn't it?"

"Aye, man it is," Bert replied.

"Where's your John?" asked Bert,

"He's playing today, but to tell you the truth, he didn't look too good this morning, so I told him to stay put and get hisself right."

"Sensible, Bill, sensible. Aye, he doesn't want to be catching his death down pit today."

William nodded to his colleague.

"Come on Bert, let's dash. A brisk walk should warm us up before we get to pit."

They both made their way toward the path at the end of Branker Street, which led the men and boys over the fields to the pit. From the end of the street they could see the outline of the shaft and workings of Pretoria through the damp of the morning mist. The night shift would just be finishing as they walked along, meeting up with other colleagues and forming little groups, all on their way to do their duty for the day. Many fathers with their sons, others alone, some of these lads were of no age, being as young as thirteen.

Approaching the pit office, one sensed that there was a good spirit lingering around the workplace with the smiles upon the faces of these miners as they eagerly looked forward to Christmas. And, there was laughter, a sound not always heard in the mornings but certainly evident today. The majority normally looked tired and weary and there was not much spirit in them, appearing sluggish and pale, but not this morning, for this morning was certainly a little different. The lads were so full of life and excited at the prospect of Christmas. With this spirit all around, in the air, and in his soul, William could feel its presence, together with the warmth of the community all around him. Today there was a more relaxed atmosphere evident throughout the colliery and he felt happy. He ventured over to the tally office to loan his tools for the day and so William reported for work.

Standing on the platform of Number Three Pit, they assembled in the cage which within seconds was dropping them into the darkness of Pretoria, and stopping off at the different levels where groups of men were working. As he descended further into the dark hole, William was thinking that in a couple more days it would be Christmas, and he was really looking forward to his break from work even though it would only be a few days. If truth be known, William despised working down the mine. He was secretly looking for alternative employment, and this was to be his main quest in the New Year. At only forty two, he was still a young, fit man. He wanted to follow his father and brother into the trade of publican before it was too late. He had discussed this many times with Mary. She had dismissed the idea of change, although she knew within herself that she would have no control over her husband's wishes. With the noise of the cage settling on the level where he was to work, William quickly brought his thoughts back to the present. Many men got out of the cage at that point and he said goodbye to some of his colleagues as they moved off in various directions. A few of the men had stayed with William to have a quick chat about life in general, or about the arrangements for a couple of drinks over the Christmas Holidays.

The 'quick' chat with the lads went on a bit too long for William so he said, "enough chatting lads, I've got some money to earn. Our Mary's seen a new pair of shoes she wants. They are not cheap, mind you, but I said I would buy them for Christmas. See you all later lads."

"Aye, Bill, see you later," the lads replied together as they all went off to work.

William began shoveling hard on the pit face and broke into a sweat only minutes into work. He always had an assistant with him, which was normally his son John, but as he was off sick, today was different. He had a young lad called Jim working with him who had just progressed to coal hewer and was now taking full pay home from the pit. Jim was twenty one. A grand young lad who had just married Ellen, who had a baby on the way. He was slowly making his way in life. Jim had proved to be a good honest lad, good workmate and a reliable colleague. He usually worked on the east level, but with John playing, the foreman had put him to work with William this day. William liked the lad, and Jim looked up to William as a father figure. These two men were not shy of hard work. It was a pity the same couldn't be said for some of the young lads who were down the pit with them. The most senior of men understood this and even they thought that young lads of 13 should not be down a pit. After all, they were just kids, the majority of men thought. Why on earth are these lads working down here? It wasn't that long ago they were having their nappies changed, their noses wiped or their hair straightened with the 'spit' from their mothers' mouths to stop it sticking up. Many of these lads had not even reached puberty.

Both men started work a good few yards away from any other colleagues, tucked away in a small level and perhaps the deepest. William was working on gathering the coal which the night shift workers had loosened before him. He was pleased with the findings. Luckily his colleagues' attempts to blast into the wall from the coal face had released a huge amount of coal.

He assessed that it would be an easy day's work. The loose coal would be easy to load into the tubs. This morning he could not believe his luck as normally it took him hours to work the face without much coal actually being mined. They both realised that if their work handling the coal could be totted up quickly they could have a couple of hours kip after lunch, so they began loading the black finding into the tub. "By Christ," William thought, as he looked down at his shovel and heaving the coal into the tub, "we have earned a mornings pay in half an hour, and there is lots more to come." Very soon their tub was full. Pleased with what he saw, he whistled to one of the 'lasher on' boys who was having a quick chat to his mates at the end of the bye tunnel. The young lad moved quickly at William's call and rushed toward his elder.

"Get this up to the surface, and I want you back here as quick as jack frost," William said. The boy didn't hesitate. William sat down on a wooden box which was conveniently placed near to where the two men were working, putting his handkerchief to his forehead to wipe away the beads of sweat that had gathered on his brow. Jim sat beside his tutor on the damp cold floor. They started to chat about Christmas and each others plans. Jim was spending Christmas with his mother and father who lived in Bolton, and after that was looking forward to the celebrations in the New Year with a predicted time in January for the birth of his child. William too looked forward to spending time at the pub and, of course, with his family.

Within a couple of minutes an empty coal tub had been brought back by James for the refill. William thanked the lad who he knew quite well from the village.

"Right Jim," William shouted, as he rubbed his hands together, "lets get to work."

Both men rose from their seating positions as William checked his watch. It was seven forty-five am. No sooner had they set about their work than a sharp, deafening noise was heard which echoed through the mine, a noise so loud that it blasted the ear drum. The ground trembled and the walls deep underground shook making the wooden pillar supports come crashing to the floor and creating a 'fog' of blackness where the once settled coal dust flew up from the floor and now swirled around them. Out of control, William and Jim were both lifted from their feet into the air and hurled toward the end of the tunnel to where they were working. With the huge force of whatever event had happened, both men hit their heads on the top of the coal face and landed heavily back on the working face.

"Christ, Jim, what in heavens name was that?" William asked.

"I don't know Bill. Whatever it was, I didn't like it!"

They both regained their composure and dusted themselves down with their hands.

"Gosh it's getting warm in here, Jim, in fact it's bloody hot. What on earth is it?"

Before Jim could attempt to put an answer to William's question, a tremendous blast of hot air was surrounding them.

"Jesus," said Jim, "I think the pits on fire!"

It only took seconds for the pair to make their way out from their place of work and venture toward the opening in the tunnel. A good number of lads had gathered at the entrance too. William felt very uneasy. He could feel the heat around him and every second it was getting hotter and hotter. His comrades had gathered into a small group at the far end of the tunnel, and he could see more and more miners joining them. Sheer panic was beginning to take hold among these men.

There was total confusion, and the fear and frustration of being trapped many yards deep underground with no means of escape began to take hold. They shouted out in vain for help to whoever, but there was no-one to hear. Many cried out for their mothers and wives, some shouted to their god. They tried desperately to find some means, any means, of escape.

Within the confusion as to what was happening, and in the midst of the intense panic of his fellow workers, William sensed the smell of something foul in the hot air. He felt dizzy and nauseous. He looked at Jim who was by his side.

"Bill, Bill! I can smell something. Its not right, Bill, what is it? What's happening?.

Without waiting for William to answer, Jim ran towards the opening of the tunnel hoping to gather answers from other miners. Within seconds of Jim leaving his side William looked toward the end of the tunnel where he could see a small blurred light which seemed to be approaching. He thought these could be flames of fire? He was right. He could see the light drawing closer and with it the heat. That confirmed his fear. Now he was fighting for breath. His lungs felt tight as though someone had wrapped their arms around him, and were squeezing them hard. His whole body was in pain. He wrenched at his shirt buttons as he tried to stagger forward toward his friend and in doing so was heavily sick. He staggered, reaching out his arm toward the wall of the pit face. Extremely frightened, he could not understand what was happening. Something terrible was going on, something was seriously not right. What was to become of him? Was it time to meet his maker?. His whole body started to shake with fear, he panicked and in doing so his bowels opened and he lost all control. There was no time to feel embarrassed. He wanted to go to sleep. He felt tired and extremely weary. It had only been a few seconds from hearing the great bang but now he could see the rolling thunder of the flames. They were no longer in the distance as a bright light but now nearly upon him and he could see them engulfing those near to him.

The dust that normally settled on the ground was now in a strange dance around William's head, igniting as it moved and burning up any oxygen that was left. He was hurting badly with the pain from the heat. The force of the flames was incredible. Jim managed to squat down to the floor a few yards from William to avoid the flames, but he was being overcome by the force of this intense catastrophe, by the strong surge of the burning gases which were now surrounding him. For the last time, Jim looked back toward his mentor, William, and from his position on the floor, he stretched out his hand as his short life on earth came to an end.

William looked toward his friend and beyond to his colleagues at the end of the tunnel. He knew he had little time left as his comrades started to fall one by one. The realisation of death was upon him as he sank helplessly to the floor, awaiting his fate. William felt the heat of the flames getting stronger and stronger until it was unbearable. He could no longer stand the pain from this intense heat, and there was no air left to breathe. The gases in the mine had now filled his lungs and surged through the whole of his body. He could feel his body tingling, his muscles started to twitch on their own accord. He became paralysed from the waist downwards. He looked at his hands, which were blurred and distant, and he could feel them shaking with nerves as he faced the thought of death. Sheer panic and fear were within him and he could still hear the cries for help from his now silent comrades as they echoed in the distant tunnel.

William slowly closed his eyes for the very last time wishing the intense pain away. He knew that at this depth underground in the Pretoria mine not even his prayers could save him. A vision of his wife and family was now before him. Then the pain was no more.

Chapter 5: It's Christmas - where's father?

Pretoria Pit had blown.

All the buildings in the town shook as though there had been an earthquake. Men, women and children were knocked off their feet by the underground blast, and in those few minutes a normal day had turned bleak with fear and alarm. The intensity of the blast caused one farmer, ploughing his fields in the early morning, to be lifted 3 feet into the air along with his plough and shire horses. The hawthorn hedges which surrounded the fields were sucked down into the ground as though they had been vacuumed, leaving them laying flat to the ground as though chopped at the stem to be taken away as debris.

Throughout the township of Westhoughton and its surrounding districts everyone knew that something ghastly had happened. They knew, without being told by any officials, that the huge bang that they had heard minutes before had come from Pretoria Pit. With some haste, the majority of people began to make their way toward the pit head. In passing, all the conversation was on one topic : "Pretoria's gone! Pretoria's gone!" There was a profound sense of shock in the community, mixed with disbelief and unease. Nearly every family in the township had a member working at Pretoria. All was confusion.

In Brancker Street that morning the doors of the houses, both front and back, were left open. Scenes of chaos and sheer panic were everywhere in the street. The villagers gathered together in groups and began making their way quickly over the fields, en route to the pit. It was a tragic scene as these poor souls, like a herd of cattle stampeding, charged towards the pit. A flurry of people, women screaming and children crying. None of them knowing what they would find, none of them knowing the intensity of what had happened. They could only guess, they could only fear the loss of life.

There was a child left standing on the cobbles of Brancker Street. She was clutching her doll, and it was her only means of comfort that morning. She had been left alone as her mother had dashed away, gone on her quest to find news of her husband and young son. For that morning, this child was forgotten.

John Gore felt sick once more as he leaned against the wooden railings surrounding the pit in which he and his father worked. It was a sickness that had nothing to do with what he had felt earlier, a kind of sickness which he had never felt before. The priest from the Sacred Heart Church had arrived at the scene, and was comforting William's wife, Mary, as she stood in a distressed state a few yards away from her son, grouped with the other Catholic families who were there too. All were waiting to see their loved ones, and all knowing that there was little or no hope for any of the three hundred plus miners who had been trapped deep underground that morning.

It was a long watch. For four days Mary Gore anxiously waited with her eldest son, John, wondering what fate had lain in store for her husband and his colleagues. She didn't want to leave the site of the pit, she was clinging on to every last hope, praying that he was still alive, that they were all alive. All the while she knew in her heart that her husband was dead. She wanted to hold him, kiss him, wrap her arms around him, and most of all to tell him how much she loved him, just one more time.

John looked at his mother with sympathy. He was becoming increasingly anxious and worried about this weakened frail creature who now appeared before him. John knew his father was dead, and thought fearfully that his mother might soon follow. Now, at just twenty-three years of age, John had to take on the responsibility of the family. He had to try to hide his grief so that he could comfort his mother and brothers and sisters. He knew it would difficult, for not only had he lost his own father, but many of his friends lay dead in that doomed pit. He wanted to cry, but the tears wouldn't flow. He was hurting with anger, hurting with grief.

John looked around at the gathered crowd. There were neighbours, townsfolk and friends, as well as other large groups of people from the adjoining towns. There were mothers, with babies held tightly in shawls in their arms trying to protect them from the cold air, young children standing confused, not really understanding why they were there, and older children looking on with tears welling in their eyes, hoping to see their fathers and brothers once more.

"I can't bear this sight," John thought achingly, "I can't bear these cries of pain, to see these faces full of sadness. These are my friends."

Repeatedly on his mind was the thought that he should have gone to work that day, on Wednesday the 21st. He had been playing, off with a dreadful cold. He and his young wife Mary had quietly agreed that morning that he should not go into work, but should keep warm inside the house. There were only a few days left to the Christmas holidays, and they thought that it wouldn't do the company any harm not having an extra pair of hands that day. John was a little reluctant to have the time off, but he was feeling the chill and he didn't want to catch pneumonia with the possibility of being sick over Christmas. So John had stayed in bed that cold December morning, with both his wife's and father's blessing, but not for long. Would you call it fate, or was it just not his time to meet his maker? The question kept recurring.

These thoughts were suddenly broken as a young lad who he knew from the pit came running toward him, shouting.

"They have brought up a couple of bodies from the west level. I heard one bloke say, 'I think one of them is Bill Gore. They were both working on that level.' Thought it best I let you know John."

Without saying a word, John rushed over to the engine house which was now acting as a makeshift morgue. He was stopped in his tracks as he collided with a young girl.

"Mister, you can't go in there yet. They have just brought some more men up and its not a pretty sight"

"I think its my dad!" John said to her.

"I'm so sorry, mister. The men in the engine house told me not to let anybody in till they said so. Can you wait here a minute and I will go and see if they will let you in. They have to take some details first to see if they can find his listing number."

John followed the girl, not listening to a word she said.

"Mister, I told you to wait there. Give these poor lads some respect, they are still cleaning the bodies in there."

John looked at the girl again. Bless her he thought, she is only doing what she has been told to do.

"I'm sorry, sweetheart," he said, realising what devoted duties to these miners she was undertaking, please hurry and ask, I'm sure its me dad".

Within minutes the girl had rushed back to him.

"Mister, the man said you can go in now." John looked at the girl who smiled up at him with so much sympathy, and suddenly he didn't want to go in.

After catching up to her son and desperately out of breath, Mary was following him toward the engine house, where they were stopped at the door by one of the Hulton Colliery officials.

"Can I ask your name and address, sir?"

"Aye, its John, John Gore. My father's William Gore. We live at 105 Brancker Street".

"Can I just say, sir, that we have reason to believe that the body in there could be your father, but we would need to be sure. Can I ask you to come through and identify him. I'm really sorry sir, but it is not a pretty sight. You will have to prepare yourself. I'm sure you will understand that the blast had an enormous effect on these lads. I'm truly sorry lad."

John sensed the empathy in the man's words, knowing them to have been spoken with sorrow and compassion. As they made their way through the doorway they were met by a couple of policemen.

"John," the gentleman said, "this policeman will escort you in."

John looked at the tall man with the kind expression upon his face, and although he was just doing his job, John could see that his eyes were red and swollen from the tears that he had secretly shed.

"Come on lad," said the policeman.

Mary started to follow her son, not knowing where to go or who to turn to, confused and saddened.

"Mam, stay there! I'll do it!" John shouted.

He didn't want his mother seeing his father. He knew what to expect. In a more gentle voice, John asked his mother to sit for a while on a chair which had been conveniently placed in front of the doorway. As she prepared to sit, he gave his mother a loving and gentle tap on her shoulder. She was obviously in a continuing state of shock and he wanted to give her what small comfort he could. He was doing his best. His younger brothers and sisters had always been well cared for by their mother, but it seemed these last few days they had been abandoned and left to fend for themselves, as if she didn't know and she didn't care. She had forgotten about life around her these dreadful past days, but John hadn't, and the children were quite warm and safe with Nanny Gore.

John walked bravely into the engine house and was met with a stench of death that he had never experienced before. He turned back, gasping, toward the door and as he did so his knees buckled under him. The policeman caught hold around his body.

"Stand tall son this won't be easy for any of us," the policeman whispered in John's ear. Recovering his composure, John pulled his neckerchief up over his nose to help disguise the smell and as he did so he turned around and saw five bodies laid out underneath white sheets on the tables. He really hoped that his father was not one of them, although he knew that soon, inevitably, he would see his father, whether it be today, tomorrow, or the day after. Not wanting to focus his eyes on the grim task ahead, he looked around the room and his gaze was drawn towards the far wall at the end of the engine house. There, at the very least, twenty coffins were placed neatly against the wall.

A young lad, not much older the 12, was holding a paintbrush in his hands. Puzzled as to what was going on, John turned to the policeman to ask, but realised before he could that the lad was staining the coffins with the sweet smell of oil.

Seeing the curious expression on John's face, the policeman said,

"it's eucalyptus oil son, because of the condition of the bodies when they were brought up. Many were badly burned and scorched. The oil just sweetens the air a little"

John knew he was being polite. Perhaps what he really meant was that some of these men were unclean, unwashed or had soiled themselves in the blast. The bodies may have been underground for a number of days and some may even have started to decompose.

"There was one young lad who sadly took most of the blast on the day of the accident. He's still waiting to be claimed, poor lad. God rest his soul."

John looked around at his comrades' sleeping bodies, all covered in clean new white sheets. On one body was a silver tin full of chewing tobacco, together with a brown leather belt.

"We have placed some items on the bodies so that their families might be able to identify their loved ones. Its going to be hard, my lad, as some have been very badly burned and mutilated," the policeman said.

All the bodies in the temporary morgue that day had been washed, and looked very clean and tidy, apart from their injuries and the burns. The medical staff and volunteers had done the best they could. The unfortunate dead had been treated with full respect. Sarah Morgan, a young pit-brow girl, had worked day and night looking after these men and boys, making sure they were clean as she laid them out one by one. She didn't want to leave her place of work, she thought she had a duty to them and her duty was well received.

John looked down towards the table as the policeman slowly raised the sheet covering a body. He recognised the lad instantly.

"Oh, holy mother of Jesus," were John's thoughts. "Surely this is not real." He couldn't look any more at this sad waste of such a young life. The sheet was slowly placed back over the face of the young dead boy as John made the sign of the cross over his chest.   It was only then that the sheer scale of the whole tragedy finally began to come home to him.

The two men slowly walked across the engine house floor and as each body was unveiled John shook his head as an answer, "no". As they came to the next but last body in line, the policeman very calmly lifted the sheet away from the body. John eyes became fixed upon his father. He looked down to the floor and recognised his pit drawers, carefully mended by his daughter, watch and tobacco tin.

The policeman said, "Is this your father?"

John replied, "Yes, this is my father."

John moved a little closer to the table. William's face and hair were very badly burned, but he was still recognisable. John put his hand out and gently stroked his face, his pure white skin was now scorched and red and with patches of dried blood upon it in some places, his thick mass of hair was gone, burned away. John inspected the rest of his body. He wanted to know how he had died, was he crushed, burned, gassed or all three?   John took hold of his father's hands.   They were so badly scorched that they had become brittle to touch and this brought tears to his eyes.   When he looked at his chest, he thought his father's ribs seemed broken, but could not be sure. Next he looked down towards his legs. They didn't seem so bad, John thought, perhaps his pit drawers had protected them, but his feet had been distorted and crushed. He could tell there were many broken bones in his feet. John didn't want to leave his father's side, but he knew he had to.

"Don't let my mother see my father. I can't let her see him like this." John turned to the policeman.

"Whatever you wish," said the policeman as he slowly covered William's body again.

"Come on, lad, lets get you into the office. There is some paperwork that needs to be signed before we can release the body."

John began to make his way toward the door to the exit, stopping to look around again at his father. He couldn't see his face. John asked the policeman to uncover his father once more. As the policeman did, John walked back towards his father and said a prayer. John had kept his rosary beads with him since he heard the dreadful news that Wednesday morning, he never let them go. They were a comfort to him. Now he said his goodbyes and words to his father in secret.

John stood up and gathered his composure. He had his family to face and bear the bad news to. The policeman patted John on his back with his hand and said, "it takes a brave man to cry and believe me, young lad, there will be plenty of tears shed over this lot. This must be one of the worst days in history and one that won't be forgotten."

They made their way over to the office.

As John left the engine house, a woman with a young child in her arms entered the make shift morgue. She grasped hold of John's hand. He knew the woman from the village, she was an acquaintance of his mother's.

"Was it your father, lad?"

"Aye, it was missus," replied John.

"They think they have brought up my John. He worked near the top of pit face. Oh this is awful, what a dreadful mess. Not my John, I keep telling myself, he was a good lad, surely our good lord won't take him?"

John had not the heart to tell her that he had seen her son peacefully sleeping, her young son who had unfortunately taken most of the blast.

As John walked slowly across the cobbles from the engine house with his mother, she looked helplessly at him. That day his own mother, only 42 years of age, looked like a lady in her eighties. As John glanced towards the grey darkened sky, tears welled up in his eyes. He slowly gathered his thoughts and remembered it was Christmas Day.

(The following words are taken from The Bolton Evening News 1910):
The heartbreaking scenes at the pit head over the build up to Christmas were more pitiful then ever as the cold light of day slowly drifted into the darkness of night. This weather, not too kind to the grieving families, a cold icy wind blew around the head of the pit shaft and all around the banking of the colliery to which these poor souls stood anxiously awaiting news of loved ones. The downpour of heavy icy rain was not to cease. There was a constant stream of people passing to and fro by the enormous growth of coffins mounting up at the side of the joiners shop, the make shift morgue. One after another, they accumulated in height against the wall, being placed there by the numerous men all wanting to help, all wanting to be active and doing their duties in respect of their comrades. The loved ones of these men in the doomed pit were en route toward other members of their families waiting for anxious news, these seekers amongst these men and boys now dead, went about their sorrowful duty. Majority had given up all hope of seeing their loved ones back alive, and their only anxiety was how to receive them, would they see them, would they see them as they remembered, or would the dark, dangerous Pretoria Pit keep them entombed for all eternity. It was, in one woman's case, a smile that came upon her face, when at last one of the coffin lids, once lifted, revealed the face of a loved one they

were searching, and even though this sight was shocking and he was unbelievably disfigured and was the most appalling sight, it was still this sight that one wanted to find, the face of their loved one. A cherished member of their family no more to hear the many joys of laughter or to share any sorrow, a special person in ones heart was no longer there to share in their life, no longer would their voice be heard, no longer here on earth where they belonged. A grief stricken mother, father, son and daughter, had to bear their grief and grieve they did thrown into their sorrow alone, they did it bravely, and tears flowed from their eyes. This grief affected many a person in so many different ways, some shed silent tears, and held composure, others cried out in vain for their loved ones, with anguish and bitterness towards who?, who was to blame?, why? The pain ripped away inside the bodies of these poor grieving souls, anguish within, desperate, broken hearts that would never heal - grief stricken lives. Many comforted by the chaplains and the great and good souls of the Salvation Army members who supported them all with their sympathy. The Salvation Army was there to support, their main concern was for each person who looked up to them with anguish, pitiful looks toward them, these people in uniform, these people of respect. Someone there to hold these poor unfortunate creatures in their arms, someone to take pity on them, someone there when they needed them, just willing them to say any words of comfort. These well respected people with the utmost admiration and of all ages did just that. Comforting words to these grieving widows, families and orphans were relayed, arms of love draped around each soul, blankets covered the shoulders of the shaking, cold frail bodies, words of comfort into each ear was spoken and a small number of lifeless corpses were brought up that evening, in total respect.

Chapter 6: United in Grief

The priest from the Sacred Heart was due at Mary's house on Brancker Street. Elizabeth and the rest of the family were restlessly awaiting news on the release of the body of their loved one from the local mortuary after post-mortem. This had ruled that the majority of the men and boys had died from CO_2 (gas poisoning) and burns, while the other deaths had been caused by the violence of the explosion.

The minutes passed into hours, and the family sat quietly, waiting patiently, not a word being spoken, the silence of death amongst them. Elizabeth suddenly broke the silence within the room by offering to make some tea, and she moved out into the kitchen. On the hob was a pot of chicken stew which she had made for the family and which had been slowly simmering since the early hours of the morning. She felt no one would eat it, since they had eaten hardly anything since the day of the accident, but she had wanted to do something, to keep active, to keep her mind stable. She had lost her son. Remembering the time when she too had lost her father at the age 15, she could also feel what her grandchildren were going through. Then her mind flew beyond the walls as she imagined what the whole township was going through? Tears started to stream down her face as she thought these thoughts. She was feeling sick and weak. How could she tell the little ones that everything was going to be alright? She walked across to the kitchen sink to wash the tears from her face, picking up a small towel on the way. She dried her face, and looked through the kitchen window to see the slag heaps piled high with coal from the Chequerbent mine. It was getting dark and in the gloom they began to look eerie.

"What a price these lads have paid to put bread and butter on the table, to have a pint of ale on a Sunday," she thought to herself.

She was jolted back to reality when, through the window, she saw Mrs Connor walking by. Elizabeth had known Mrs Connor slightly as she had lived in Manchester Road, near to the Stag and Griffin. She was walking, bent over, between two young men who Elizabeth didn't recognise. She went to the back door and as she opened it shouted:

"Mrs Connor, Mrs Connor, are you all right?"

One of the young lads turned to Elizabeth, and tipped his cap as a hello gesture.

"Evening Missus. My name's Albert. We're helping Mrs Connor back home, she's just identified her son and grandson, my cousin. They brought them out this morning. She's not too well missus. I'm her nephew and this is my brother John."

Elizabeth was lost for words. All she could do was to look on with sympathy.

"Please," she cried out, "Please just wait there a moment."

She scuttled back into the kitchen and got a large cooking bowl from the cupboard. She turned to the hob and with a ladle scooped out a good few helpings of the chicken stew and quickly covered the bowl with newspaper and walked back into the yard. She opened the back gate and gave the bowl to Albert.

"Here, please take this and make sure she gets something warm in her belly."

"Aye, missus, I will. She needs something warm, she has been at the pit head every day since Wednesday, waiting and waiting. It's dreadful, this disaster! I can't imagine what folks are going through when I think about all those families who have lost someone. Have you lost someone, missus?"

"Aye, I have lad. I have lost my son, William."

Changing the subject quickly Elizabeth said, "Go on, get her back in the warmth and make sure you get a good fire going for her. Will you be staying with her tonight?"

"Aye, we will, and thanks missus, you've been very kind. God bless."

"Tell Mrs Connor, I will call and see her soon to make sure she is alright. Look after her lads, she needs your support"

"Aye missus and thanks again."

The lads turned away and started to walk again. Mrs Connor had never spoken. From her facial expression Elizabeth could tell that she was in deep shock.

Poor woman, thought Elizabeth. She turned and closed the gate and began to make her way back into the house. As she was about to close the back door, she heard pitiful screams. Looking through the dusk she could just make out the figures of people returning from the pit head having just learned the fate of their husbands and sons.

She bowed her head to rest on her chest, and her tears started to flow again. She clasped her hands tightly and walked back toward the door. As she closed it behind her, she could shut out the terrible noise of the whines and cries from these women and children.

Elizabeth sat down on a chair in the kitchen, and tried to regain her composure, but it was too hard. Her tears were now in full flow, and her body ached from her cries. As she cried she bowed her head and through the tears that she cried for her son and all those others, she saw the small basket belonging to Mary. Beside it lay the patching material ready for applying with the needles and cotton within.

A gentle knock came on the front door. Elizabeth jumped up, rapidly wiping the tears from her eyes and dusting herself down quickly with her hands. She fixed her grey hair and made sure that she was respectable to receive the priest. As she made her way towards the parlour she was met in the hallway by her grandson John.

"I'll get the door, Gran." He rushed toward the front door, and as he did so, Kitty ran to her grandmother and held her hand. John opened the door and the priest entered the hallway.

"Please, Father, go into the parlour. Is there any news of my father?"

The priest looked at John, his sad eyes showing how hard it was for him to cope with the tragedy which had happened to his flock.

"My dear children," he said, "Shall we pray for the soul of William Gore."

The whole family knelt as the priest blessed them all. After a few seconds of prayer, the silence was broken,

"Where's my dad?" asked John for a second time.

"I have just got news that the release of your father will be this afternoon, and that a service will take place at the Sacred Heart tomorrow at 11am with a burial at Westhoughton Parish at 12 noon. The body of your father will be collected from the mortuary and brought here this afternoon for the family to pay its respects.

"Mary, I am truly sorry for your sad loss. Be assured that the thoughts and prayers of our Catholic community are with you and your family today, and through this terrible time."

At these words, the tears started to flow from every eye. The priest left them quietly in their grief for a while and then slowly made his way toward Mary. He knelt down beside her and placed his hand onto hers.

"Mary, I know that I am perhaps intruding on your grieving, but may I ask, Mary, regarding flowers. Would you like me to arrange some for you?"

Mary nodded,

Elizabeth saw the look on Mary's face and it worried her. She moved over toward Mary and sat down beside her. She also held her hand. Mary looked pitifully at Elizabeth and burst into tears again.

"Why on earth would He take my William? Why? I thought God was good. If He is so good, why has He done this? Why has He caused all this harm to all these families? Why should I pray to Him when He has taken my husband, and left these poor things without a father? There is no justice here, there is no God. If there was, He would have saved everyone, all of them, and not left them to die"

"Shush, shush, love. I know you feel pain and anger, I do too, he was my son. God has a place for everyone in his kingdom, and no one knows when or why we are called. But when it happens, Mary, we go - and with our faith behind us we stand proud, knowing we will see our loved ones in eternity," whispered Elizabeth.

Elizabeth looked at her priest. He nodded to her and got up from his kneeling position, slowly making his way toward the door. He said to John,

"Look, lad, if you need me for anything more, please don't hesitate to come for me. I will be here to help and support you and all the other family members. I will leave you in peace, and look after your mother. Your grandmother is a wonderful woman. I am sure everything will be alright."

John thanked him as he made his way toward the door.

"See you tomorrow, Father," John replied.

Just before John closed the door to the priest, he looked up toward the top end of Brancker Street. He could no longer hear the children laughing, or see the young ones standing and chatting amongst themselves. All he could see were women walking, crying, with children in tow, their heads all bowed down to the floor, being comforted by other members of their families. John watched the priest walk out of sight then he gently closed the door behind him.

"Gran, Mams right," said Kitty, "Why should we pray to God when He has took pa? He never did anything wrong."

"Kitty, my love, please try and understand. Everyone has pain and hurt when we lose someone we love, and there is an anger inside us that we need to take out on something or somebody else. All the anger and grief we have inside has to come out of our soul, and this is what is happening to all of us, especially your mam. She didn't mean to say these things, but at the time she felt she had to and this has released some of her anger. Come my love," she turned to Mary, "let me make you some tea and have some warm stew."

Mary followed her daughter and Elizabeth, not knowing what time it was or even what day it was. It was the 26th December, Boxing Day.

Number 79 was the home to Charlie and Alice Wilkinson who originally came from Staffordshire. They had moved to Brancker Street in the early 1900's to work in the pits in Lancashire. They had one son Charlie Jr, aged 14, and two young daughters Alice, aged 9, and Ellen, aged 6. Both father and son worked at Pretoria, with father working nights and son part-time during the day.

Ellen was known as Nellie to her family and friends and was the youngest member of the family. A sweet little girl, full of life and mischief. The street called her 'the tornado', and for

70

good reason as she ran everywhere she went. She could never stay still or in one place for more than five seconds. Alice, her older sister by two years, was a little more shy and quiet. Mother Alice would often say to her neighbours and friends about Ellen that she didn't know where she got her energy from, but she was always rushing around, here, there and everywhere. She can't keep still, she is like a tornado, a huge one at that!

This family, unknown to themselves, were the talk of the street. This was not in a nasty way, but through the tales Alice would tell her friends about their family goings on. One neighbour on the street, Mrs White, one day found Nellie in the kitchen with a kitten which Nellie had found roaming around the back gates of the houses in a sad state. This little cat looked undernourished and weak and had obviously lost its mother. Nellie nicknamed the kitten Sandy, an unusual name for a black and white cat, but Sandy it was. The two sisters fed the cat daily on bread and milk, and the weak little kitten soon realised it was on to a good thing and got to know its place in the world. However, there was one day when bad weather in the form of heavy downpours lasted all day and as Sandy lived mostly outside in the coal bunker in the back yard, he was soaked to the skin by the rain. Nellie brought the poor creature into the warmth of the house. In her infinite wisdom and thinking that she was being very clever, she fetched a wooden clothes' peg from her mother's peg basket which was kept in the larder. She then carried the wooden clothes' horse, which was always standing nearby the hob, over to the kitchen fire. Nellie then held the kitten and carefully gathered the loose skin hanging around its neck, and pegged it to the clothes horse, moving it closer to fire. In her mind, the cat would soon dry out! The screams from the kitten could be heard at least three doors away, and if it hadn't been for Mrs White, who was walking past the back gate at this time, the kitten would have cooked.

With the back kitchen door already open, Mrs White rushed into the room. She stood in shock, not believing what she was seeing.

"Oh child, whatever are you doing?"

Nellie answered "I'm just drying Sandy out. He got a bit wet today and I don't want him to catch a cold"

"For goodness sake, Nellie, this kitten wont die of a cold. Get him down from there now. He will set on fire.

The kitten was screeching from the shear pain of the peg which attached his body to the clothes horse, Nellie tried without success to undo the peg, but the kitten was having none of it. It scratched her dainty pale little hands and soon drew blood from her nimble fingers. Mrs White moved toward the clothes horse and grabbed the kitten with both hands, covering its paws so that he would scratch no more.

"Right Nellie, undo the peg."

Nellie didn't hesitate. This time the kitten was set free. Mrs White put the kitten onto the patterned oil cloth on the kitchen floor, and as she did, it scampered away toward the kitchen door. The kitten ran away, out of the back yard through a hole in the gate, and was never seen again.

On the 26th December, Nellie and Alice had received only a couple of presents originally intended for Christmas Day. Christmas, for some reason, was not the same this year. They thought Pa was in a very bad mood, and Ma kept crying all the time. Ma and Pa had both been missing from the house for long periods of time over the last couple of days, and they could not understand why. It seemed that one minute, Ma was there, and then the other minute, Pa was there, but not together as usual. Then again, brother Charlie had not spent Christmas with the family this year, not that there was a Christmas. Nellie thought this was all very strange. Charlie was always around. He was fourteen and Nellie loved him. She knew something was wrong and had tried to ask a number of questions over the past few days, but no-one had ever answered them.

"Ma, why is everyone in the street crying? Where has Charlie gone? Why is he not here?" Her mother had not told Alice and Nellie the real truth of what had happened, and that Charlie was never coming home. She had told her daughters that he had gone away. Away in her words meant Heaven.

Charlie's body was recovered on the 25th December, the same day as William Gore. The girls' father, Charlie senior, survived the disaster of that fateful morning because he had just finished the night shift.

Unknown to the girls, the coffin of their brother Charles had been brought to the house that afternoon and placed in the parlour. He was to be buried on the morning of the 27th and in the light of this Alice and her husband had a few calls to make in the village. They intended leaving the children on their own, as they would be gone no more than an hour and neighbours could be relied upon in any emergency.

The children were out in the back yard getting coal for the fire, one of their many household duties.

Alice shouted to them: "Your father and I have an appointment in the village. We should be no more than an hour. Don't go roaming the street. I want you both to stay here till we come back." Both girls nodded.

Nellie finished her duties and wandered back into the house. She washed her hands in the kitchen sink and then wiped them on her pinafore. She liked being alone in the house, although she was glad her sister was there, it made her feel so grown up.

She wondered what to do next, should she go outside to play, but then again it was cold and none of her playmates had played out in the street for a good few days. What has changed she thought to herself, why is there no laughter anymore? Why did Billy from up the street not call on Charlie anymore, he was always around at our house? Why did she and Alice get sent home from school that day sooner than planned, and why was Pretoria so important? Everyone was talking about Pretoria.

Nellie skipped into the parlour and suddenly stopped in her flow as her eyes met a long wooden box laid upon the dining table. What a huge box, she thought, whatever could be in it ? She moved a little closer to investigate. It wasn't wrapped up in Christmas paper, but perhaps it was too big to wrap up, she thought. It's a surprise. I knew it, I knew it, Santa has been after all, she thought!

She rushed out of the parlour and ran down the hall into the kitchen where she hoped to find Alice. She wasn't there. She looked though the kitchen window to find her still in the yard brushing the coal dust back into the shed.

"Alice, Alice, I have found another present. Come, come and look, it is big." Alice put the brush down on the stone flags and rushed into the kitchen.

"What do you mean Nellie, we have had Christmas!"

"No we've not. Santa has been again and left us something in the parlour. I knew he would not forget us, I knew it"

Alice got very excited at the prospect of having a present. The two young girls ran out of the kitchen, down the hall, and in their eagerness, they both got stuck in the passageway on route to the parlour.

"Wow," exclaimed Alice, "that is a big present."

"Perhaps it's Charlie's present. He wasn't here for Christmas was he. Perhaps Santa has brought it for him?" said Alice.

Both girls climbed onto two of the six wooden chairs that surrounded the oak wooden table and looked down at the box in awe.

"Well, there is a name tag on it. It says 'Charlie Wilkinson, aged 14," Alice said. "I don't think we should open it if its for Charlie."

"Oh go on, shall we open it Alice?" Nellie asked, looking inquiringly toward her sister. Alice looked at her sister with excitement and puzzlement. Her eyes had never fixed upon such a huge box before, and certainly not one which she or any other person in the family had ever received. What could it be? She thought. She bent over and put her hands on the table. As she did so, she noticed a strange smell, an unusual aroma she couldn't make out. Alice put her head a little closer to the box and began to sniff at the wood. Funny she thought, this unusual aroma reminded her of the larder. She jolted back quickly. She was now quite certain of herself.

"I think its from the butcher," said Alice confidently, "we didn't have turkey on Christmas Day, did we Nellie, ma and pa were feeling sick, do you remember?"

"Gosh, yes I do, we didn't have Christmas dinner, did we? I remember, we had sandwiches and Pa went to work that day didn't he ? He has never worked on Christmas Day before."

With a leap of imagination, Alice suggested "Perhaps there have been no turkeys in the village and they were late in fetching them. So here it is. Charlie must have ordered it for ma and pa. Perhaps he had bought it for them for Christmas," Alice said.

Nellie was not amused at the fact that her sister had come up with the possibility of a turkey being in the box. It wasn't a present after all, a fact now confirmed by Alice.

Nellie reluctantly said, "We may as well open it now and put it in the larder for ma?"

Alice thought this was a good idea.

Nellie made the first move, putting both her hands on the corner of the lid. It moved with ease. Alice, wanting to help her sister, grabbed the middle part and slowly slid it toward her. As it opened, the girls were met with an unpleasant smell which made them turn their faces away from the box. They were still completely unaware of its contents. With the lid partially covering their find, they both looked toward the box. Nellie fell off her chair with the absolute sheer shock of what she could see. Alice could not believe her eyes. She did not know what she was looking at. A very badly mutilated figure was lying there in the box. Nellie ran out of the parlour and into the hall screaming for her mother, even though she knew she was not in the house. Torn between her sister's screams and the desire to look more closely, Alice looked down at the figure and began to realise that it was her brother, Charlie. Yes, this was her brother, and he was dead. Why? How?

This family was not the only household to be affected. Nearly every house in Brancker Street suffered a loss, as did the majority of houses in Westhoughton, where there were families who were grieving for the loss of a father, son, uncle, or brother. The neighbouring towns of Atherton, Deane and Bolton also saw casualties, but the majority of lives taken were in Westhoughton and Wingates, a thriving little community close by with its own parish church.

Since that fateful day in December, the whole town was brought to mourning. Christmas was cancelled for the majority of these families. Nearly every house in the village had their curtains drawn across each window as a mark of respect for the dead. A community in grief, a community sadly never to be the same again.

Funerals were now being carried out every hour in the local churches, where all faiths combined as one. There were funerals carried out on Christmas Day. The wives, girlfriends, mothers, brothers, sisters, and fathers of the deceased supported each and every household. The churches were packed to full capacity, with some mourners standing outside in the cold of a winter's day to pay their last respects. The air was full of the cries of grieving families walking behind their loved ones coffins. Women fainted, children screamed and strong proud men wept openly. These were scenes beyond belief. In the graveyards, men joined forces and helped the local grave diggers with the enormous task of digging the new graves for these unfortunate men and boys. They had worked on through the darkness of night ever since that day of the disaster, the labour going on for twenty-four hours without rest. The men worked around the clock in shifts. None of them did it for pay, they wanted to do it out of respect. This was a community united in disbelief, united in grief.

The coffins in which lay the bodies of these men and boys were being lined up day after day, hour after hour by the side of the churches, waiting for the journey to their final resting places. The sound of the horses' shoes on the streets as the carriages carrying the coffins were pulled through the town was a constant reminder of this continuous procession.

Some poor men and boys were still entombed in the pit, and the rescue operation was still ongoing day and night with many local volunteers helping with the search. Suffice it to say that as each body was uncovered and brought to the surface, it was only for it to be buried the day after. The local undertakers found it difficult to cope with the amount of coffins that were needed and supplies were brought from other nearby towns.

Surrounded with the stench of death in the cold damp air, Elizabeth stood at the doorway to the Sacred Heart Church. As she glanced around she could see many friends, all with tears filling their eyes. She held her daughter-in-law's hand tightly, knowing this day was not going to be easy for any of the family, but especially for Mary. As she turned, she could see William's coffin too, which lay in the funeral carriage covered with the beautiful wreaths of flowers with cards attached each written with a sympathetic message.

William's coffin was carried into the church by his sons, John and William, by his brother Thomas and his brother-in-law Charles, and was closely followed by William's family and friends.

The church service was one of sadness and the reality, of what had previously been the sheer shock of what had happened that dark morning in December, finally sank in. The priest also found the service extremely hard to deal with, and stopped many a time in mid-flow to clear his throat or wipe away a tear. Tears flowed down the faces of every family member and the rest of the mourners as they tried, without succeeding, to sing the hymn 'The Lord's My Shepherd'. Everyone had eyes swollen and reddened through the tears of previous days. The women that day had pale skin as though undernourished, and there was no sign of the usual ringlets or bright dresses worn for church. No hats this day, but the usual sight of shawls draped around the heads of the women.

William's coffin was carried out of the church by the pall bearers for his final journey. It was lifted into place on the waiting hearse, where the horses harnessed to the carriage were patiently waiting the duty command. Then they would move off down the route to the Roman Catholic cemetery in the grounds of St Bartholemew's Church.

As the funeral party approached the church gates they were met by numerous mourners who had just attended the funeral of two other victims from the disaster. These young lads, aged only 17 and 15, had just been laid to rest. As William's family walked into the churchyard they could see another funeral where not only one, but two, coffins were being carried into the church for the service. Elizabeth was acquainted with the family and knew that the poor woman had lost both her husband and her son. With respect, the family waited until the party disappeared into the church, then they moved on towards William's final resting place.

William Gore was laid to rest with an abundance of mourners and his family around him. The weather was not too kind that day and it had started to rain, the sky looked heavy and was very dark. Elizabeth thought it might snow later that day, as there was a bitter cold, icy wind blowing. As Elizabeth looked around she could see many people, hundreds, wanting to pay their respects, not just to her son William, but the ones laid to rest in the hours before and the ones to be laid to rest in the days to follow. These mourners have been out in the cold weather all day, thought Elizabeth. If they are not careful it will be them who are being laid to rest as well. She felt the warmth from their presence around the church graveyard and knew she wasn't alone in her grief. She was brought back to the moment with the strong loud voice of the priest as he conducted the final prayers as William's coffin was lowered into the ground. As the coffin descended, Elizabeth knew that the time had come when she could no longer control her emotions. She had been strong for the whole family over these last few days, but was now letting go and saying goodbye one final time to her son. She wept and wept uncontrollably. Elizabeth Ann took hold of her mother to comfort her, while John took hold of his own mother, Mary, who was also weeping along with her children. It was the most heartbreaking scene anyone would wish not to encounter. The faces of these young children, swept into grief so early in life, losing their father in these circumstances, was beyond any child's imagination and thoughts. They really couldn't understand why their father was no more here.

That month of December, nearly every household in the area said goodbye to a precious family member.

Chapter 7: The Price of Coal

It was now March 1911 and the death toll was 344. Mary Gore had received a letter requesting her presence at a meeting arranged at the local court house of Bolton for the following week. The purpose of the meeting was to sort out the Compensation Claims for the families affected by the disaster at Pretoria Pit. The contents of this letter requested that she must bring to the meeting any related correspondence and details of all the family members in the household. It was also a request that she bring with her confirmation of the amount of money coming into the household in any form.

Mary was accompanied to the meeting by her son, John. They boarded the regular daily train which travelled from Chequerbent Station to the nearby town of Bolton. On their arrival at Bolton Station they disembarked at the platform and made the short journey by foot northwards towards the centre of town. On the way they came across many widows, mothers, sons and fathers who Mary seemed to recognise from Westhoughton. All were making their way to the great Edwardian building situated in the centre of Bolton. Obviously, Mary realised, she was not going to be alone as she had once thought. She became a little upset at the thought that she no longer felt like an individual in this quest of grievance but more like a humble beggar in her fight for justice.

Both mother and son made their way through the cobbled streets toward the Court. They were both amazed to see how many motor cars there were on the roads, and the large number of shops and department stores which displayed the finery and luxuries her family could not afford.

Mary had been to Bolton only a few times in her life. She remembered the occasions when both William and herself, with their eldest son John and his sister Elizabeth, had taken the train to the town and then ventured out onto the huge park to be found just outside the centre. She had made sandwiches and cakes and packed them into a small picnic basket with the homemade lemonade, a favourite with all the family. It was a picnic enjoyed by all. They would sit on beautiful lawns of the greenest grass and it was a real tonic to feel the rays of the sun on one's skin. Mary and William had found great pleasure in watching both children run freely and picking the flowers which, she could remember, had the sweetest smell. They could afford these little luxuries then, but as the family grew and more children came along the chance for luxuries in life diminished.

These dreaming thoughts quickly ceased as they entered the magnificent stone-built building through a doorway at the side. Here, within the hallway, there were scores of people engaged in intense gossip. Mary looked around in amazement. As her eyes passed over each person, she found that she could quite possibly say that she knew a small portion of these people by name. The rest of the gathering she recognised as faces from her local town, but she could not put names to the faces. She could sense the immense chatter and gossip amongst the women, and she knew that nothing would be missed. A little sad really, Mary thought. The townsfolk would get to know other people's business and if they didn't they would find a way to get it. As she looked over toward these people, she hoped dearly that they were not talking about her and her family, but she could feel that once she had been recognised, the conversation would veer toward her.

Mary and John scoured the great hallway and found the few rows of chairs placed on the parquet flooring. Right above the chairs was a large oil painting of King Edward V11. All the chairs had been taken and were being used by the frail and elderly. Mary turned to her son and asked, "What do we do?"

He replied, "I would assume they have appointments scheduled for each family. Stay here Mam and I will try to find out."

John left his mother standing in the hustle and bustle of the crowd of people and made his way toward a girl who looked as though she was an office clerk. She was standing near to the stairs carrying numerous files in her hands which were obviously full of paperwork. She looked extremely ruffled and nervous with her duties that day.

As John approached her, she said, "hello Sir, do you have an appointment today?"

"Yes," replied John,

"Right, sir, could you please give me the name of the deceased."

"William Gore."

"Thank you sir, and what is your relation to the deceased?"

"He is my father," said John.

"Thank you," she replied. "Can I ask you to please take a seat in the hallway if you can. We are extremely busy as you can see. I will report to the officer that you have arrived and they will call you when they are ready to receive you."

"Thank you," John replied.

The girl smiled at John and he returned the smile. A sweet little thing, he thought, a dainty little creature, not much older than eighteen. John retraced his steps back towards his mother who he saw talking to a group of women in the centre of the hallway. As Mary saw her son approach she smiled at him, an expression that John had not seen upon his mother's face since the day of the accident.

As the clock ticked away, the minutes and then the hours, they noticed that the large amount of people gathered was slowly diminishing and found that there was room to sit on the chairs, a welcome luxury instead of standing. No sooner had mother and son sat down than the clerk, who in secret had pulled one of John's heartstrings, appeared at the top of the stairs.

"Mr William Gore deceased, abode 105 Brancker Street, Westhoughton," she called.

John stood to his feet as though on parade being summoned by a sergeant major.

"Could you please come upstairs into the office, they are expecting you".

As John waited for his mother to get up from her chair, he brushed his clothes down with his hands, and then combed his thick mass of auburn hair. Both slowly made their way over to the office clerk who in turn led them upstairs toward the meeting room. John linked his mother's arm into his and they made their way through the large office towards the huge wooden oak desk which was situated centrally at the far end of the office. The wall behind had two oval shaped stained glass windows with many panes of coloured glass separated by small streams of lead, allowing the rays of winter sun to filter through into the room, brightening every corner. The men looked up at them and smiled with sympathy. Mother and son returned the compliment.

The men in the office party were seated in a line behind the desk, and all stood to welcome them. There were four officials: the representative solicitor of the late miners; the Hulton Colliery Company Management representative; and two other officials who Mary and John had not seen before. As they approached the desk, a grey haired, small built gentleman with an upturned moustache asked them both to take a seat and make themselves comfortable. When they were both seated, this gentleman and his colleagues all followed suit.

The gentleman asked as he looked at Mary, "are you the widow of William Gore deceased, address 105 Brancker Street, Chequerbent who was sadly killed in the explosion at Hulton Colliery No 3 pit on the 21st December the year 1910?"

"Yes Sir," was Mary's reply.

"And you Sir ?"

"This is my eldest son, John, Sir," Mary replied before John could answer the gentleman's question.

"Mrs Gore, Sir, I have been instructed by the various officials who are involved in this case, and with all cases relevant to the miners who lost their lives on the morning of Wednesday 21st December 1910. It is our purpose in this meeting to arrange what necessary compensation payments are to be made to each member of the families of the deceased miners whose lives have been terribly affected by these sad happenings. Mrs Gore, we have upon record that you have seven children, is that correct?"

" Yes Sir," replied Mary.

Looking towards her son, he asked, "do you have the relevant paperwork that was requested you produce at this meeting?"

"Aye, I do Sir," John replied.

As John unfastened his jacket buttons to reach inside to one of the pockets, he fumbled with nervousness. He produced a bundle of paperwork which had obviously seen better days and handed it to the gentleman. The man smiled and nodded as a thank you gesture toward both. He then engaged in a long, whispered conversation with his colleagues seated behind the desk.

The conversation between these official parties continued for what seemed like five minutes to Mary and John, until the main speaker looked up toward them and cleared his throat, breaking the silence.

"Mrs Gore, Sir, we have indeed reached a decision which has been agreeable to all parties here. It is that compensation will be made in payment on the following terms. You have been awarded a lump sum payment of £226.00 to be invested in trust. On this basis, you will be allocated one pound and five shillings per month from this fund for the upkeep of your family. This is also based on the fact that you have three older children working and residing at the home address and that you are in receipt of their monies. Is that correct Mrs Gore?"

"Yes sir, my three eldest children do work, but my son John is married and will be looking out for a house of his own soon, and he will no longer be living with me."

"Mrs Gore, we have to make this decision of compensation to be awarded to you on the basis of what monies you have coming into the house, not what might happen in the future. Do you understand?"

"I do Sir, but what about when my son leaves home?"

"The compensation payments have to be awarded based on the facts in front of me here today. The amount you have been awarded is for loss of life by accidental death of your husband, for each child under your care, and the compensation payments to substitute your husband's weekly wage. Mrs Gore, do you understand? "

Mary broke down in tears.

Mrs Gore, I fully sympathise with you on the sad circumstances which have taken place and believe me when I say we are here to help. You seem to have a loving family by your side in these sad days and I am sure with the love of your family you will be lessened in your grief!"

Mary looked toward the gentleman, her eyes fixed upon his. How could she be, 'lessened in her grief,' she thought.

"Sir, if that is what is to be awarded to me then so be it. I feel more money should be awarded, not only for the loss of my husband, but for the pain and suffering that he would have felt, deep underground. My youngest children shed tears every night. How do I explain to them that their father is not coming home. No one knows my pain or grief. You Sir and gentlemen, may possibly have wives and families at home and once you have finished your business here today with all these casualities of the mine, you will fold your paperwork away in your desk drawers, lock the door to this nice warm office, and leave in your fancy motor cars to drive to your home, where I feel your wives and children will be waiting to welcome you. I don't have that any more Sir. Yes, my home is filled with children, but those poor creatures need clothing and feeding, and they are without their father, and I am without my husband and companion. Do you know Sir that I cry myself to sleep every night, wishing, hoping, that it is all a bad dream and that he will one day return to us."

"I also hear my next door neighbour, a young woman in her twenties, just married last year with a one year old son, sobbing her heart out every hour of the day, and throughout the night, but to whom. She has no family to rely on. You tell me Sir, that with the love of my family, the pain of grief will ease? My pain will never ease. Sir, my William, in good health and in the prime of his life was taken at Pretoria Pit and at what price? To earn his way in life, to put food on our table, and clothe his family. He had to pay the rent on our house, and the loan of

87

his miners lamp and tools at pennies per day, all owned by the Hulton Colliery."

"You see, Sir, Pretoria has taken everything from me and our family. I doubt, Sir, that you will ever understand my feelings, and by God do I pray that you may never find yourself in the unfortunate wisdom that I find myself here today. Thank you, Sir for your sympathy, but it will not bring my husband back to me. I abide with your decision, sir, I take it there is no other choice?"

Mary rose from the chair on which she had been seated and nodded towards the gentleman.

The officials looked at Mary, all slightly embarrassed, with the fact now upon them of the truth of her words. Their once pale white faces now flushed.

John turned and looked toward his mother in awe and astonishment. He could not believe what he had just heard flowing from his mother's mouth, these words came deep from within her heart and soul. He had never in his whole life seen a woman fight so for her own justice. He was proud and saddened, but most of all, he welcomed the words spoken from his own mother to be a true and accurate record of not just her feelings, but the feelings of ever single person who had suffered from this unbelievable event which was to change these unfortunate families' lives forever.

John no longer felt that he was there to support his beloved mother, he felt that he was the weaker one of the two. His mother had fought this battle and won, although they were not to receive what they were expecting in the way of compensation. The money offered would not replace their loved ones, but equally they could not live without it, little as it was in anyone's eyes. No more words were exchanged between mother and son. No other words were needed.

They both made their way toward the door to exit. One of the officials rushed to the door in haste and opened it. Before they walked through, Mary's eyes veered toward the roaring fire to the right of the room. As she looked at the fire she could see the coal burning upon it, a glowing of red and orange colours intermingled with the blue and yellow flames. At the side of the fireplace, upon the hearth, sat a large brass coal scuttle which held many pieces of coal. Mary bowed her head once again and thought of her husband. Did that coal come from the Pretoria mine? Did her husband's hard toil of his last living days now keep these wealthy gentlemen warm in the bitter cold months of winter. Would her pain of grieving ever go away?

Mary and her son walked through the door with their heads held high. Justice, in her eyes, had been accomplished. She had now, for the first time in her life, relayed her true feelings of hurt and betrayal to these total strangers. She would now face the next battle of life with her head held high.

The compensation awarded to Mary and her family was a far cry from the one pound and four shillings which William had earned each week. John, Elizabeth and William were all working full time which helped the family purse, but Seth worked only part time, and Kitty, Francis and Thomas the youngest were all at school and so were left to make do with the shillings awarded from the fund.

In the aftermath of their meeting at the Court, the whole family gathered at 105 Brancker Street late that afternoon, anxious to hear of the days outcome. Elizabeth in her thoughtfulness for her family, had that morning made a selection of sandwiches with newly baked bread plus some flat currant cakes and fruit scones which would nicely complement the homemade berry jam which was one of her specialities.

Thomas, Elizabeth Ann and Sarah, all with their spouses, were seated around their mother's dining table under the window in the parlour. Their children seemed to be keeping themselves amused with toys outside on the cobbles and, although the sun was still shining, dusk was almost upon the community. It was still a bitterly cold afternoon with an icy feel in the air. The children might be oblivious to the cold on their delicate skin, but they were well wrapped in woollens just as a precaution. As the family sat to eat the food so lovingly prepared, Mary thanked them all, especially her in-laws, for their help and support over the last few weeks and expressed how obliged she was for their kindness and sympathy.

In the midst of the ongoing conversations, Elizabeth looked at Thomas. She thought he seemed extremely quiet and deep in thought and was not contributing to the talk of the days happenings around the dining room table.

"Thomas, are you alright?" she said.

"Aye, mam, I'm all right."

"Come on lad, I know when something is gnawing at you, what is it?"

The conversation, in mid flow around the table, suddenly seemed to quieten down till it ceased, their heads turning towards Thomas and his mother. Ester, Thomas's wife, looked down toward the table and slowly clasped her hands.

"Thomas ?" Elizabeth asked inquisitively.

"Mam, it's nowt. Just leave me alone." So saying, Thomas quickly rose from the chair and hastily departed from the parlour towards the kitchen.

Elizabeth got up and followed her son.

"Thomas, in God's name what on earth is wrong with you?"she demanded.

"Mam, this is really hard, and I don't know how to approach the subject."

"Thomas!" this time with a stern voice from his mother, "I beg you to tell me what is wrong?"

"Mam, this really does put me in the most awful situation. Our William owed me over one hundred pounds."

Elizabeth was shocked at these words spoken by her son. She looked at him in disbelief. It seemed there was a silence as of the dead of night around the house, until it was broken a few seconds later by Mary's arrival in the kitchen. Mary looked toward Thomas.

"Thomas, what did you just say?"

"Mary, I am so very sorry."

"Sorry about what?" asked Mary.

Thomas looked toward his sister-in-law and knew he had to carry on this conversation, and as he did so his eyes welled with tears.

"Our William had accumulated debts of £112.00 pounds which he owed to me. It was all the effect of his drinking and gambling habits which had paid a heavy price. He had never been totally honest with you, Mary. I am so, so sorry. I wish I had never lent him the money. He swore and begged me to secrecy so I was to tell no-one. He had promised to pay me back as soon as he could. I was hoping that I did not have to tell you all this, but it has left me and the family short of cash and our Ester has found this week that we are to have another child."

Mary collapsed in a pathetic heap onto the cold oil cloth which covered the kitchen floor tiles. Thomas quickly ran to his sister-in-law's aid, accompanied by the help of his mother. The rest of the family who had moved from the parlour into the hallway to assuage their curiosity, slowly turned their heads away with embarrassment. John had overheard the conversation between Thomas and his mother and quickly shouted to his grandmother to make a hot strong cup of tea as he made toward his mother lying helplessly on the floor. Elizabeth quickly followed instructions, and left the two men to carry Mary through to the parlour where the family were already preparing the chaise longe to receive her.

"This will kill me mam, can't you see?" John roared, with tears rolling like a small stream down his face. "This will kill her!"

Chapter 8: A New Beginning

After the catastrophe at Pretoria pit, Elizabeth's life changed dramatically, and the community of the village was never to be the same. Her family, and the majority of this small township were deprived of their loved ones, and where there were once united, loving and warm family gatherings, they were no more. All deteriorated in the face of death. The situation forced many to change direction, sending their future into many and other winding paths. It was all a far cry from the laughter once heard on the cobbled stones of Brancker Street. This once unique and happy community had been shocked into a profound sense of anger, of poverty and resentment. Where was the love that once shone through each family member? Sadly now, love and laughter were little to be seen!

Pretoria pit had left these poor families as, 'Victims of the Mine'. The accident that day had put an enormous strain on their lives as they desperately missed and grieved for their loved ones, their men and boys no longer breathing had been snatched to their final resting place by their great God Almighty, many being taken far too soon.

Everyone joined in sympathy and support when and where they could. Children were sent to stay with other members of their family to ease the burden, and so the community coped as a joint effort. These families that were once held together with the presence of a father figure, a brother or a son, were sadly no longer so tied. Many were now totally torn apart, and for what price?

William's widow, Mary, once, a youthful looking mother in her early forties, so full of life and spirit, was now reduced to a frail woman, suffering very poor health since the day she lost her husband. The cold and damp days she had spent at the pit head eagerly waiting, longing for news of her husband, had certainly contributed to the deterioration of her health. Elizabeth feared for her daughter-in-law's welfare and this worried her. The shock of the disaster, together with the birth of nine children, of which two had died at a young age, had taken a heavy toll on the frail, weakened creature she could now see.

With advice from her mother-in-law, Mary and her family, William Jr, Elizabeth, Kitty, Seth, Frances and Thomas moved out of their lodgings at Brancker Street to 156 Bolton Road, Westhoughton, a small terraced cottage. Living with too many memories of her late husband was the main reason for this uprooting and moving. She hated the sight of the Pretoria pit in the distance, the smell of coal which surrounded her daily, and the constant reminder in the shape of the slag heaps which she could see from nearly every window in the house. Her husband's friends and colleagues, who had been 'lucky' and escaped the blast, had all returned to work and maintained their daily routine of meeting on the corner of each street, and walking to their place of work. The railway line which ran in front of the houses was a constant presence, seen through her eyes every day when she opened the curtains to let in the sun's rays. Every day she could see the trains which transported the coal to all areas of the country, coal which had once been mined by her husband from Pretoria pit. All these sights reminded her of Pretoria and the past. Also to contend with were the people turning up daily in the village to stare at the working classes in their tragedy. Men in fancy suits and hats with their wives, dressed up in their silks and embroidered finery came to see the peep show, with the bereaved as the star attraction.

They would turn up their noses at the sight of a sombre-looking woman, babe in arms, with a shawl draped over her head to keep herself warm. Mary thought of the community, once bonded in love and shared hardship, hand-me-downs and poverty. The strangers knew nothing of this. The survivors of the tragedy still worked twelve hours a day to provide for the basic needs of their families with very little left for luxuries.

Who gained from their lives of toil and hardship - not the miners or their families and what was the true price of coal, Mary thought.

She never forgave! She had lost all faith in her God. "It was His will," that was all she ever heard from her priest, "it was His will." The 21st December was a day that would be forever etched in the minds of so many townsfolk. The day of that awful disaster, that had taken her beloved husband and the father of her children, was set to take a loving mother to an early grave.

Mary suffered frequent panic attacks triggered from the day that she had received her husbands corpse lying in a plain wooden coffin. His body had been badly burned in the explosion and the sight had effected her deeply. These attacks had put a huge strain on her heart, and this was coupled with the fact that bronchitis was now upon her and she was developing pleurisy. Her children and her doctor feared the worse. Elizabeth could feel that her daughter-in-law was slowly drifting toward death, and in spite of having tried on many occasions to pull her daughter back from this extreme grief, she knew it was a helpless case. No matter what Elizabeth said or did, she knew Mary had given up hope, love and life itself. She did not want to carry on her struggle in life. Until the day of the disaster Mary had seemed in perfect health, but the toil and bitterly cold days spent at the pit head waiting for news had certainly taken its toll. The immense grief that she had suffered also affected her heart - a heart that had once beat so strongly for her whole family was unable to do so any more. It had been God's will to take a husband and father in the prime of his life, and it was once again God's will to take Mary Gore into His arms, and she died in April 1911, just four months after her husband's death. She had lost her fight to struggle on in life. Pretoria took these brave men and boys by accident on that fateful day, but on this day it also took a loving wife and mother.

In April 1911 Mary Gore was laid to rest with her beloved William. The warmth of the spring air had brought out the daffodils and tulips which made a beautiful, colourful pathway in the church yard on the way to her final destination. She was followed by her true faithfuls, her children and family, who had all made this journey once before in December. They could still see the heaps of flowers on the newly dug graves of their father's comrades, some of them not having long been laid to rest. Her children's cries could be heard from every corner of the churchyard, their painful screams melting the hearts of each family member present and even the onlookers, who had come to observe the happenings that day shed a tear for these orphans.

As they exited through the lych gate onto the cobbles of Market Street, little Thomas glanced toward his Grandma and said, "where has my mother gone, Gran? And why has my dad not come home? Where are they?"

Elizabeth could not answer her own grandchild as tears filled her eyes once more. She looked down towards him as he walked with his elder sister Elizabeth. She reached down and put her loving arms around him, picked him up from the cobbles and wrapped her shawl around him, giving him a huge hug.

"Why don't you come back to my house and we shall have some cakes to eat. I baked some specially for you this morning. And I think I have a spare shilling in my purse. I think we might just call at the sweet shop on the way home and get some chocolate just for you."

Thomas smiled at his gran, and as he did he slowly returned the hug. He really didn't know why he was walking along the street, or in fact why he had just attended church. Elizabeth smiled lovingly towards him and then turned to look at her other grandchildren walking at the side. She smiled on each and every one on them.

As John walked behind his grandmother, his head was racing with emotion and his thoughts were on life in general. He linked arms with his wife Mary and then, his glance moved from her face downwards to the shape of their unborn child. He smiled as they strolled along in this huge family group. He turned his head to look towards his grandmother, his aunts, uncles, cousins and brothers and sisters, all walking together but silent in their own thoughts. Surely no more heartache could possibly come to this family. John being the eldest was now head of this unfortunate family and he felt he had suffered enough heartache and pain over the last few months. He thought he could cope with the loss of his father, but to lose his mother in such a very short time after was beyond belief.

When his mother, Mary, had decided to move away from Brancker Street to her new lodgings in Bolton Road, John and his wife Mary had managed to find a small rented house in Park Road, quite near to his Aunt Elizabeth Ann, who now lived at a small farm holding called Hilton Nook Cottage, in Waters Nook. With the expectant news of their new baby's arrival due at any moment, times were becoming extremely hard. He had not worked since the day of the disaster at Pretoria and was determined not to set foot near the place again: in truth, it frightened him. The rent for their house was being paid weekly by his wife's father, a grand gentleman who was not short of a penny or two. "Just until we get on our feet," John would say. He knew he had to provide for his family, and living off someone else's means was not what he wanted in life. It was up to him to provide and he did not want charity. The only work he knew was coal mining but there was no way he would consider Pretoria as an option for employment. His thoughts turned to a new life. What about America? Uncle Pete and Uncle John have done alright for themselves there. This he knew as the many letters exchanged between them since they left Chequerbent had always come with good news. What more is there here for me?

A few days after the burial of his mother, John was sitting by the fire at their cottage in Park Road and Mary was busy doing the household chores. "Mary please sit down. I have something I want to talk to you about." Mary looked toward her husband and was a little surprised at his words. Normally the two of them, if they had something to say would talk around the dinner table, or during the conversations of the day. With a worried look on her face, Mary turned toward her husband, What's the matter John?" she replied a little apprehensively. "I think we should go and live in America, near my Uncle Pete and Uncle John." Silence entered the room. Mary was stunned to hear such words spill out from his mouth. Nervously laughing Mary replied, "Oh don't talk rubbish, we are alright here, and besides, our family are here, and your brothers and sisters need you here. And don't forget, John, I am having a child. How can we go to America with a new born child? Don't talk daft. You're just being silly. Take that nonsense out of your head"

Mary carried on with the chores, and chose not to sit down with her husband. "Mary, for goodness sake woman, I am serious. What have we got here? What is there left? We don't own a home, I don't have a job, I have no parents. We could make a better life for ourselves in America, I know we could." "Now you're talking silly. What about your brothers and sisters, William, Elizabeth, Seth and the young ones? And don't forget John, these children have lost their father and mother too. It's not just you, you know. Not to mention your Nanny Gore. What on earth would they do without you? Uncle Thomas would miss you, and your Aunts Elizabeth Ann and Sarah would dearly miss you. Get that nasty thought out of your head right away. Don't talk any more rubbish!"

Mary wanted to clear from her head all the words she had just heard from her husband, hoping he would not mention the subject again. John did as he was told, and didn't mention the subject again that evening, but a chapter had been opened in the book within his head, and he wanted to read more.

Their first child was born that year, a boy. John called him William after his beloved father. He beamed with pride as he held his new son in his arms for the very first time He was a father, he was so proud. He cried once again, these tears were full of mixed emotions, joyous at the thought of his young child being brought into the world, but tears of sadness that his mother and father were no longer there to share this happiness. He thought of his child, how he would protect him and look after him, this dainty little creature with a mass of black hair, and gorgeous blue eyes. John thought he was a true Gore. The child looked so much like him but even more so like his father, William. John's thoughts as he held his son were most of all that he must treasure every moment that he had with him. One thing in life he had learned since the death of his parents was to enjoy the love of life and treat every day as though it was going to be the last. He thought about his own life, and the life of his young son William, where would it lead? Would he follow in the footsteps of his father and grandfather before him, working as a coal miner, down the mine 12 hours a day starting at the age of 13? Or would he for once change this pattern and choose his own destiny. John was about to make the biggest decision of his life: it was time for a change, a new beginning beckoned, and his first port of call the following day was to Nanny Gore.

Over the few days that followed Elizabeth has many conversations with her grandson, John, about his thoughts of a new life in America. His brothers and sisters turned a blind eye to his suggestions, thinking that it would never come to anything. They too pushed their brother's words to the backs of their minds, hoping in secret that the fact of the matter would slowly fade away. The younger siblings did not get involved with these conversations and were totally unaware of their oldest brother's intentions. Elizabeth was really unhappy and feared losing another member of her precious family. She turned to spending most nights in the company of her now oldest son, Thomas, and the convenience of his public house. It was her way of coping with a family in turmoil, a family that in her eyes was now being slowly ripped apart.
Seated in the lounge area of the bar in the Stag and Griffin one late evening, John and Elizabeth were in the midst of serious conversations. Elizabeth was begging John to stay to look after his brothers and sisters, but John had decided that could not stay in the village of Chequerbent. There was more to life than coal.

"Nan, I need to get away. I have lost my dad and my mam, I have lost my friends. Uncle Peter and Uncle John are over there and I ain't going to work at Pretoria no more. You and our William are here to look after the household. Our Elizabeth and Kitty are all going to help and the younger kids, our Seth, Thomas and Frances will do just fine. Nan, we are Gores, don't forget. We are, and have all been strong, and that isn't going to change. I'm sure they will all look out for one another. They always have and always will. But I have got a life too, Nan, and I don't think living it here in Chequerbent is the best way forward."

"What about Mary and young William? What does she think, what are her feelings?"

"She doesn't want to go Nan, but I have told her that if she doesn't like it we can come home. I have promised her faithfully. Our William will have a good start in life with the fresher air, and it's not as though we are going over there without any family. Uncles' Peter and John have both said that we can stay with them awhile until I find work. Nan, I love you so so much, but I have to go. I will write regularly, like Uncle Peter and Uncle John, and you never know, Gran, once I have made enough money, I will sail over on the boat and take you back for a holiday. How about that?"

Elizabeth knew that no matter what words she could find to say to him, her grandson had made up his mind, and there was no way she could change it. She broke down in tears at the thought of losing her eldest grandchild as she looked into his gorgeous piercing blue eyes and put her hands through his thick head of hair. Secretly he had always been her favourite. "How handsome you look, our John, what on earth will I do with out you. You remind me so much of my William, in fact you grow more and more like your father each day. He would have been so proud of young William and so would your Mam. I do miss them all so much, you know."

"Aye, I know, Nan. I miss them too, but they are right here," pointing to his heart, "right here, and that is something no one can take away."

Elizabeth reached into the pocket of her dress and pulled out a white cotton handkerchief. She gently raised it towards her eyes and dabbed away at the few tears that had been shed. John too brought his hand up toward his eyes and caught a tear with the back of his hand before it managed to roll down his cheek. United in emotion, they both leaned over, their arms around each other, and hugged. Not one of them wanted to be the first one to come out of that embrace.

From behind the bar, Thomas could see what was going on between his mother and nephew. Trying to look casual, he walked over to where John and Elizabeth were sitting, and moving a chair from under the table, he slowly sat down and placed both hands on the top of his thighs. "Well John, mam's told me about you wanting to go over to America. Are you sure you have thought it through, lad. Don't you want to wait a while and let things settle down here a bit? It's a bit soon lad. With the new baby, I mean, and your mam's barely cold in her grave?"

"Uncle Tom, I have a wife, and a child, but I have no mam and dad. I'm not going back to work at Pretoria, I hate the place. That place took me dad and most of me friends. My life now is my family, our Mary and our William. The others will cope. They are Gores don't forget, Uncle Tom, tough, hard nuts that can stand their own ground. I love them dearly, but I don't fear for them at all. They will make in life what they want to make in life and besides, there is plenty of family here for them, including you Uncle Tom, Nanny Gore, Aunt

102

Elizabeth Ann and Aunt Sarah. I have spoke with them all these past few weeks and they have given me their blessings"

Finally, Thomas looked at his mother and then at John. He put his hand out toward John, took hold of his nephew's hand, and shook it like a true gentleman. Well lad, I will miss you, you know that don't you?"

"Aye, I do Uncle Tom, I will miss you too. But I will come and visit when I can and you are more than welcome to come and stay once we get settled."

Thomas turned to his mother. "Well, mam, this lad will make a life for himself and that family of his. I can feel it in my bones. He's got a sensible head on his shoulders. It's a pity his father wasn't like him. Now I don't mean that in a bad sense you know John, what I mean is with his gambling and sorts. God rest our William's soul."

Thomas cleared his throat. John could sense he was fighting back the tears, not just for his own brother and but also for him. He knew Thomas. He was a great fellow, but where tears were concerned, he would be having none of them.

Elizabeth asked her grandson what were his next plans. Well Gran, I am just waiting for a telegraph from Uncle Peter. He has the dates for the ship's sailings over the next weeks. Uncle Peter said that he would like to come over in the summer months, said he wants to stay a few days in Chequerbent so that he can see the family again. He was coming over for a visit anyway, as you know Nan. He said in the letters he had wanted to visit when Dad died, but couldn't get a ship over in time. John kissed his grandmother on the top of her head as he rose from his seat. "Right Nan, will see you later. I will bring our William. Aunt Elizabeth Ann has knitted some clothes for him, and she asked me and Mary to call round. We will call in after. It will be around 6 o clock."

"Aye, see you later lad," Elizabeth whispered, not raising her eyes to his face.

The mother of William Gore's wife was Mrs Gallagher. She was a widow herself and nearing the age of 70. She had been born in Southern Ireland, was a practicing Catholic and was known as Rose Ann to her friends and family. She had moved to the area of Lancashire whilst her husband William found work in the coal mines, and stayed when he had died some twenty years previously. Rose Anne also lived in Brancker Street, three doors down from where her daughter once lived at 105. Although close by in the street, she had suffered from failing health and this had kept her from much involvement within the family. Over the years her grandchildren's visits to her home had been minimal. However this was all destined to change now that her grandchildren were orphans. She and Elizabeth Gore became good friends and companions in the care of the family. Many nights, these two women would meet and spend hours in each other's houses sharing the daily gossip which had emerged around Chequerbent. They even strolled to mass together every Sunday in the summer months, and became a strong presence in the weekly Catholic Mother's meetings. These two women held an equal love for their grandchildren, and now shared equal responsibility. After the sad death of their mother and father, the grandchildren soon got to know their Grandmother Gallagher's house very well and became accustomed to family meals there as well as frequent sleepovers .

John Gore now lived thousands of miles away in America, making his way in life with his wife and son. This left William, the second oldest son, as head of the household and the father figure at the young age of 19. The orphaned grandchildren had already settled into their new home in

Bolton Road, and the family seemed to be coping well although it was a pitiful enough scene in a house with the absence of a mother or father.

The priest often called on the Gore family home, and offered help and advice when needed. The Mayor's fund, which had been set up since that fateful day of 21st December, was there as a back up in any emergency. In the event it turned out that, in all honesty, when help was needed, it was provided. The older boys and girls provided for the family, and the Pretoria Compensation Fund helped a little. Their uncle Thomas and his wife made sure the children were in the best of health always and their Aunts, Sarah and Elizabeth Ann acted as substitute mothers. The whole family were committed to each other, brought together by the tragedy of Pretoria, a commitment that was never to be forgotten. John wrote regularly to his family. Every letter was welcomed and although thousands of miles away over the sea in his new home of Pennsylvania, his face was forever etched on their minds. And as well as all this, their trusted grandmother was always close at hand.

For Elizabeth, Number 59 Brancker Street was no longer a loving home full of laughter and warmth, but had become a dark cold place that had an unpleasant sense of unease. To her it was full of memories of the happy times spent there, but in most recent months these memories had been soured. She wanted to move to new lodgings. Rose Ann was already now happily residing with her grandchildren at Bolton Road, and she thought it might be wise if she herself moved to be a little closer to them.

In May 1912, Elizabeth went to the colliery office at the top of Brancker Street and handed in her notice to leave the premises of number 59. Her new abode was to be Hilton Nook

Cottage in Waters Nook, a few minutes walk from Brancker Street, where she was to live with her daughter Elizabeth Ann, her husband James and their children. It had been discussed between the family. Thomas and his wife were extremely busy at the Stag and Griffin, Sarah and her husband Charles also held a heavy burden of workload with their business at The Bluebell public house in Wigan. This left Elizabeth Ann, who welcomed the idea. She was at home, and her mother would be able to help with the household duties, and she would get a little extra money from her mother as a way of keep. Elizabeth would certainly take pleasure having her daughter's six children around her and in the same household, yet she was only a stone's throw away from the young Gore's residence in Bolton Road. A five minute walk over the fields from Water Nook and she was at their door. This suited her perfectly. A little happiness was again about to enter her life. It seemed only yesterday that she was sat in the parlour of No. 59 thinking about spending time with loved ones and having Christmas together as a family. What a huge difference she thought, since December 21st when her whole life had changed so dramatically. So Elizabeth Gore made a great move. Thomas and Elizabeth Ann had arranged to collect her belongings and all was arranged with the help of family and friends. Her few clothes were placed into boxes and the furniture in the household was equally divided between her son and daughters.

Hilton Nook Cottage was a beautiful old stone building of 1782. A small cobbled path led the way to the most enormous red painted double-fronted door. The house was not overlooked by neighbours and was surrounded with an acre of land. Although Elizabeth Ann and her husband James had not purchased the building, they had a lease on the cottage which they rented from a colleague of his. It was quite a large, brown, brick house, complete with a barn and stables. There were four bedrooms upstairs which were adequate with one for the husband and wife, one for Elizabeth's privacy, and the children shared the other two bedrooms. What a luxury she thought.

Downstairs was a large kitchen, with oak beams set into the walls and the ceilings, exposed brickwork on every wall made the cottage unique, and there was an array of large York stone flags displayed in a pattern of chequered squares set into the floor. In the centre of the kitchen sat a large dining table which could seat their growing family. It had taken James many months of concentrated woodwork in the barn to build it. From the kitchen, a doorway led to a further two rooms. One of the rooms overlooked the beautiful garden which had a central garden pond containing some small fish. Wild flowers grew in abundance in the area and there were a number of fruit tress that had been planted throughout the garden. These were now full of the new pink blossom which foretold that by the late summer months apples and pears would be plentiful. There was a small living area adjoining the main living quarters which Elizabeth Ann had converted to a play space for her children. When the children had gone to bed, the room was taken solely by James and provided a place where he could relax and read the paper after dinner.

Elizabeth now sat in the living quarters of the cottage. It was a strange feeling, she thought to herself, not having control over her life, an uneasy feeling, tense and somewhat apprehensive. She remembered the days when she took her first steps along the cobbles of Brancker Street, with her family in tow. Then there were smiles and eagerness on everyone's face. There were so many happenings around her, and life had changed so much. She felt very vulnerable. But once again she could feel the comfort of the farm life she once knew as a child. It was wonderful to look through a window and see flowers, a nice change from the coal slag heaps at Brancker Street.

Over the next few years Elizabeth wrote regularly overseas to her sons, Peter and John, and her grandson, John. They had all settled satisfactorily. Peter, and his wife Elizabeth, visited England regularly, her son, John, returned to England just the once, but grandson, John, never returned. Peter, being a home bird always liked to travel to England, and every time visited Chequerbent to see the cobbles in Brancker Street. He liked the fact that his mother was safely looked after by his sister, Elizabeth Ann, and her husband, James, and that his late brother William's sons and daughters were now making their mark on life. They had sadly lost their grandmother, Rose Ann, a few years ago, but these children coped well. He was glad to see life for once was being kind to all and that his mother's smile was once again on her face. His young nephew, William, was now married, as was Elizabeth. Seth was living life as a handsome bachelor and courting a young girl called Mena. Frances and Kitty were working hard at the mills, and both were now courting young men and lodging near to their places of work. Sadly, Thomas, his youngest nephew had died in 1914, aged 14.

Peter was pleased to be once more in England, and he was pleased for each member of his family. Although they were separated by many miles, there was an enormous bonding within this unique family. He was amazed to see that his sister, Elizabeth Ann, had produced nine children, and his elder sister, Sarah, had five, all of them well loved and cared for. They had been brought into the world with love from their mothers, and all behaved with the most outstanding good manners.

In 1920 Peter was staying at Hilton Nook Cottage with his wife, Elizabeth, and daughter, Margaret, who was now 16 years of age. Two years previously his brother, Thomas, had died and was buried opposite his other brother, William, who had died in Pretoria pit. His older brother, John, had managed to get the fare over and had attended the funeral when Elizabeth had written to tell him of the bad news, but unfortunately Peter had not had the chance to come over then. Thomas was 42 when he died, the same age as William.

Whilst on this visit, Peter travelled around the township of Westhoughton, visiting each member of the family before he had to return to America. He hated to say his goodbyes once again. He had enjoyed seeing his family and was extremely sad to leave. Elizabeth was now in her late seventies and she did not look the picture of health although she must be a tough old boot! Bless her, he thought, this woman who had suffered so much heartache in life. I don't know how she has managed to survive. He felt that he should not be leaving her.

Peter stood in the doorway of Hilton Nook cottage with his wife and daughter by his side with their baggage. It was a mere holdall, but had been enriched with a few items of food which Elizabeth Ann had prepared for their journey. They were due to set sail from Liverpool the following day. He threw his arms around his mother and kissed the top of her forehead, giving her an enormous hug. In Peter's thoughts he knew this would be the last time he would see his mother. He feared for her health. Elizabeth Ann came to the door with her children following behind. Mary the oldest, now 19 years of age, followed by Charles, Jack, James. William, Peter, Thomas, Elizabeth Ann and the latest addition Joseph. His nephews and

109

nieces all gathered around and while the older boys shook hands with their uncle, the girls kissed him, and young Joseph being 2 years old, was picked up off his feet by his mother who cradled him in her arms. Peter moved closer to his sister and gave her a kiss. Baby Joseph stretched out his arms in the most loving way and wrapped them around his uncle. Peter could not help but reach out for the child. He picked him from his mothers arms and held him into the air. "What a bonny lad this one is. I wish I could take him home," he said jokingly.

Elizabeth Ann laughed, "I would not part with any of them. These children are my life. Its been hard work, our Peter, but I wouldn't change anything. Yes, me and James have our ups and downs, and the money has often been a little tight, but we have always got by. They are good children and we are a good team. They all have their own jobs around the house and that helps me a great deal."

Peter placed his young nephew back into his mother's arms and blew a kiss to her. Well, my loves, I suppose this is it. Off back home, as they say. Always in his thoughts, however, was his true home, Westhoughton. "I am going to call on to our Sarah's before I go." Elizabeth began to cry. "Hey Mam, don't cry, you will set me off next. Look, as soon as I get home I will write to you."

No more words were exchanged. Peter took a step back to allow his wife and daughter to say their goodbyes. This time the tears really did flow from all parties. Peter's life, as he knew, was in America.

In 1921 Elizabeth Ann found that she was expecting again, and Elizabeth wondered how much more her daughter could take. Giving birth to nine children was certainly taking its toll on her body, and her immune system was at an all time low. When her youngest child Sarah was born, Elizabeth Ann took to bed rest on the advice of her doctor, but James could not understand what was wrong with his wife. He did not ask any questions, apart from who was going to cook his supper. James thought women were there to cook, clean and produce children and he had never once given a thought to the hard labour his wife had gone through. She had been pregnant ten times since they married in 1899. Elizabeth Ann was now weak and frail and it was her mother, Elizabeth, who had full charge of the younger children until her daughter's health returned. This was also putting a great strain on her health, for she was no longer young.

Elizabeth Ann did recover from her weakness, but in her appearance she remained extremely frail and wan. The colour was gone from her cheeks. She looked painfully thin, and her once shining, piercing dark brown eyes, which glistened in the day's sun like the stone of onyx, were now embedded into their sockets. Her hair, which had once been so thick and the darkest brown, was now slightly greying and had a very fine texture.

Elizabeth spoke quietly to her son in law James about how she feared for her daughter's health. She asked him politely, on more than one occasion, to 'leave her alone' for a while and let her get back to health. James did not understand and wouldn't listen. Elizabeth Ann never refused her husband.

February 1923 was one of the darkest days in Elizabeth's life. She could hardly stand at the graveside of her beloved daughter, Elizabeth Ann. She had to lean heavily on Sarah, the only daughter left. She could not believe what was happening. Her daughter who had been just 43 years of age, in the prime of her life, was now gone. Taken to an early grave in these cold months of winter. Elizabeth looked at the poor children, ten in number, who were huddled together around the open grave. The coffin had been carried on a cart by two beautiful horses and was now laid in front of them ready to be placed in the coldness of the earth. She had seen this picture before with her father and sons. These children were now without a loving mother, the youngest child, Sarah, only two years of age. She cried painful tears for her daughter, herself and the children. She looked around the graveyard as the priest once again gave his blessing to their great God Almighty, this time for the life of Elizabeth Ann Harper. She could not acknowledge his prayers. She scanned the ground with her tear strained eyes, looking around the earth on which she was standing. There were beautiful flower arrangements from family members, friends and neighbours. Her eyes now flooded with tears as she glanced at the nearby graves. Here were her children, William, Thomas and now Elizabeth Ann, all buried in the ground beneath her feet. Her sons Peter and John in America could not get to the funeral in time, nor could her grandson John, but all sent their condolences and flowers. Would she ever see them again? She feared not.

Elizabeth sat at the table inside the kitchen on Hilton Nook Cottage thinking of the family she had loved and lost. The older children had gone to work and she was left to take care of Joseph who was due to start school in the August of that year and his younger sister Sarah, aged two. It seemed there was no more laughter, fun and love within this household, but bitterness, anger and resentment. This had become a cold house. Gone were the days when she was happy in life, when she first moved to Chequerbent with her husband John and young family back in the late 1800's. The joy was rekindled once more for just a few seconds as she thought again of her path in life. To Elizabeth a waiting game had emerged. What would her God, who she had worshipped throughout her life, cast down for her next challenge? Why had her loving God and trusted Friend made her walk though life such an awkward passage? She was filled with a sense of doom as she wondered what other problems He would put in her path, and how much more she could take. It seemed to be a waiting game with which Elizabeth did not feel at ease. She felt weak and was becoming frail, and at the age of 78 she felt her time on earth was nearing its end. She became very humble.

That February the weather outside was not kind. It had been a cold harsh winter and some bitterly cold winds had arrived to add to that month's misery. Elizabeth had just put more coal on the fire and thought of the children. She thought this was a job that should be done by James, but she could not complain, after all she was living there under his roof.

Young Sarah was starting to get a little restless and Elizabeth thought it would be good if she took a nap for an hour. She beckoned her granddaughter to come into the back room so that she could put her on the couch with a warm blanket. Sarah soon settled, leaving Elizabeth and her youngest grandson Joseph in the kitchen.

Elizabeth sank into the rocking chair which was conveniently placed near the coal burning stove in the kitchen. Joseph quickly followed her and looked up toward his grandmother. Elizabeth called to Joseph and patted her lap, inviting him onto her knees. Joseph, always eager to please and with a loving smile on his face, rushed at the chance of spending some quality time with his grandmother.

Elizabeth looked down at her grandchild, and as she did she put her arms around him and gave him a big hug. "Gran, please can you tell me about my mam, and why she's not here anymore?" Elizabeth had heard these pitiful words before and softly answered, "Yes love I will," but before she could start speaking Joseph looked up towards his gran and asked, "Gran, where did you live when you were little? Did you live on a farm like this? Did you have a mam? What was she called? Where is she now? Did you have any brothers or sisters like me Gran? Gran?" Joseph looked up at her, pleading for her to answer. "Eee, God bless you, our Joe," she whispered as she placed her loving warm hands upon his beautiful youthful face, and tears starting to well in her eyes, "where would you like me to start love?"

" At the beginning, Gran, start at the beginning."

Wigan Old Market Place - This postcard shows the town of Wigan, with the
Parish Church in the background. The King of Prussia Inn
is just out of sight to the right. (Author's own collection)

Market Street Westhoughton - 'The Heart of the Village of Westhoughton'.
(Author's own collection

Park Road Westhoughton - Park Road was a main road through the
village that led to Chequerbent. At the end of this road was The Stag &
Griffin Public House. (Author's own collection)

The village of Chequerbent. The Stag & Griffin Public House and the
Mission School. The entrance to Brancker Street is just out of view to the
right. (By permission of David Smith, Author)

'The Explosion' -Hulton Colliery Disaster 21st Dec 1910. (Author's own collection)

The Parish Church of Westhoughton, St Bartholomew's - Many funerals of the Miners took place here along with many burials. The grave of the unidentified victims is in the centre of the churchyard.
(By permission from David Smith, Author)

117

The Lych gate at St Bartholomews - Over one hundred and twenty coffins passed though this gate in the weeks after the disaster. (Author's own collection)

Westhoughton Parish Church - St Bartholomew's interior view. (Author's own collection)

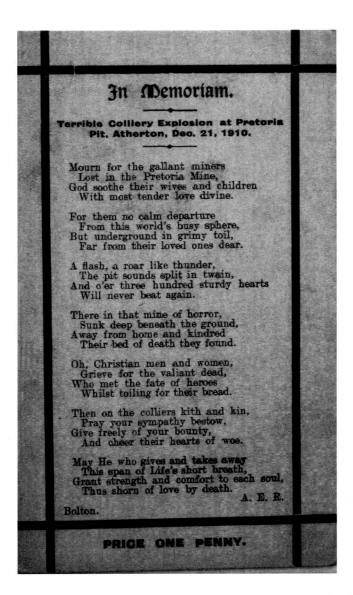

In Memoriam.

**Terrible Colliery Explosion at Pretoria
Pit, Atherton, Dec. 21, 1910.**

Mourn for the gallant miners
   Lost in the Pretoria Mine,
God soothe their wives and children
   With most tender love divine.

For them no calm departure
   From this world's busy sphere,
But underground in grimy toil,
   Far from their loved ones dear.

A flash, a roar like thunder,
   The pit sounds split in twain,
And o'er three hundred sturdy hearts
   Will never beat again.

There in that mine of horror,
   Sunk deep beneath the ground,
Away from home and kindred
   Their bed of death they found.

Oh, Christian men and women,
   Grieve for the valiant dead,
Who met the fate of heroes
   Whilst toiling for their bread.

Then on the colliers kith and kin,
   Pray your sympathy bestow,
Give freely of your bounty,
   And cheer their hearts of woe.

May He who gives and takes away
   This span of Life's short breath,
Grant strength and comfort to each soul,
   Thus shorn of love by death.

                    A. E. R.

Bolton.

PRICE ONE PENNY.

In Memoriam - This is a postcard sold near to the entrance to Pretoria Pit to
raise funds for the widows and orphans.
(Author's own collection)

In Loving Memory of The Men and Boys (over 300).
This postcard was sold for one penny to raise funds for the families of the victims by retired miners.
(Author's own collection)

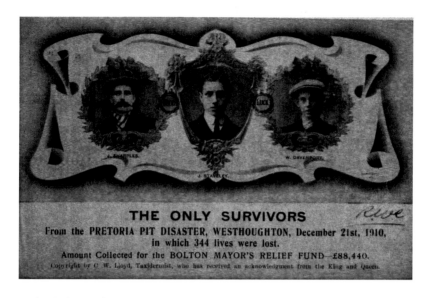

The Only Survivors - Postcard to raise funds for the widows and orphans.
(Author's own collection)

The Grave for the Unidentified Victims. This photograph shows the newly
dug grave with flowers before the Monument was erected. You can see the
children behind looking at other newly dug graves, perhaps of their loved
ones. (Author's own collection)

HULTON COLLIERY DISASTER.
TOMB OF THE 13 UNIDENTIFIED BODIES, WESTHOUGHTON CEMETERY.
P. Westhead,   G. Gleaves,
Chairman,   Ex-Chairman,
Westhoughton District Council.

The Grave for the Unidentified Victims. This photograph shows the newly dug grave with flowers before the Monument was erected. You can see the children behind looking at other newly dug graves, perhaps of their loved ones. (Author's own collection)

The Pretoria Pit Rescue Team. (Author's own collection)

122

Wrightington Hall & Bridge. To the right of this postcard was
Wrightington Hall. Seth Clarkson was buried here in the Catholic
Ground. (Author's own collection)

BRANCKER STREET

These extracts are taken with kind permission from the Editor-in-Chief of the Bolton News February, 2007.
What follows was written exactly as it was presented at the time when printed in the Bolton Evening News 1910-1911 and written by a Bolton Evening News reporter at the scene.

Wednesday 21st December 1910

DISASTER AT HULTON PITS
350 MEN AND BOYS ENTOMBED
HEROIC RESCUER LOSES HIS LIFE
FIGHT WITH THE FLAMES
BRINGING UP THE DEAD

A terrible explosion occurred at the No 3 Yard Mine at the Pretoria Pits of the Hulton Colliery Company at Over Hulton, shortly before eight o'clock this morning. There had previously gone down the pit about 300 men and boys. A large number had also descended the Arley Mine which is connected by the shaft with the Yard Mine in which the explosion occurred so that altogether seven hundred lives were in danger. The immediate effect of the explosion, which was terrible and heard a long distance away, was to stop the fans which were forcing air into the Yard Mine and gas and dust commenced to spread immediately from the mine to the Arley Pits. The mouth of the Yard Mine became filled with debris and a rescue party which was immediately organised and went down the Arly Pit found it could not make its way into the Yard Mine. Efforts were therefore directed to get the men out from the Arley Pit and by half past ten they had - all four hundred had been brought to the surface. Many of them were suffering very considerably from the effects of gas poisoning and were attended to at the surface by doctors who had been summoned from the surrounding townships, and encouraged by women who came to the pit laden with blankets, coffee and other hot drinks for the men.

Up to this time only one death was reported - the head fireman in the Arley Mine, who lived in Church Street, Westhoughton, an elderly man who was found near the pit mouth dying from the effects of gas and he was dead before he got to the surface. In the morning men had been busily at work clearing away the debris from the Yard Mine and the rescue party made heroic efforts to penetrate into the working in the pit where the explosion occurred.

Grave Doubts of saving the men

Some colliers who know the mine are expressing grave doubts as to whether any of the three hundred will be got out alive. Fire was found to be raging at the bottom of the mine and the conditions altogether are very much against the progress of rescue work.

The Gathering Crowds

Scenes at the pit mouth are very pathetic. Mothers and wives and sisters from Bolton, Westhoughton, Atherton and Chequerbent and the surrounding districts are there weeping and wringing their hands and waiting for news. There were many touching scenes as men brought up from the Arley Mine were recognised by their relatives.

Very slight hopes

Hundreds of people have assembled on the pit bank and the surrounding fields and are waiting with utmost anxiety for any item of news that may dribble through. Their hopes, however, are very poor for they feel that if there was any chance of the men being got out alive something would have been heard before now. The officials are most anxious as to the conditions underground and at four o clock feared there were very slight hopes of anybody being brought out of the mine alive.

Sombre Christmas

Writing at the scene of the disaster one of our representatives says:-What a sad Christmas this will be for many homes, was the first impression that arose in one's mind when the news which spread throughout the county like wild fire was realised. Joy turned into sorrow for many a happy family. The sad stories of horror have caused untold regret, the accident ranging amongst the most terrible of colliery disasters. The boom of the dire explosion was heard distinctively in Daubhill (approx 2 miles) and as far distance as Ellenbrook and immediately crowds of horror stricken relatives hurried breathlessly to the scene of the shocking affair, which only a few hours previously had been one of industry. The explosion was heard in parts of Farnworth and Leigh and Tyldesley and residents in the immediate district felt the vibration quite distinctly.

An Evening News representative interviewed a colliery worker who was on the spot when the explosion occurred and he graphically described the affair. He said, "I was working on the pit-bank at the time and my attention was attracted by smoke coming from the up-cast shaft. Suddenly there was a deafening explosion and smoke and flames belched forth as though the shaft had been a LIVE VOLCANO." Huge pieces of timber were flung so high into the air that some were deposited on the adjoining winding house. It was an awful experience and so violent was the effect that the winding apparatus was thrown out of action. It transpired that the guide at the foot of the shaft had been shattered and then it was

126

evident that no winding could proceed in the uptake, in which is the winding shaft used for the ill fated mine. It was estimated that about three hundred and fifty miners were engaged in this particular mine at the time of the explosion and a number of officials proceeding by way of the down-shaft lost no time in attempting by the connecting road to reach the workers, but they quickly discovered that there was no hope of getting at the men by that means as they were met by dense volumes of smoke and gas which was impossible for a human being to penetrate.

A ray of hope was cast over the gloomy foreboding by the fact that when a couple of cage birds were lowered into the uptake-shaft where the explosion made itself heard, they were hauled up little worse for their experience. They were left underground for twenty minutes and proof was therefore forthcoming that the air had not been fouled in the immediate vicinity of the shaft, but rescue was improbable until the hauling gear had been restored and the ventilation arrangements put into operation again.

Bands of rescue parties, BRAVE FEARLESS FELLOWS who were prepared to face death for the sake of their fellow workers, and gentle banded nursing sisters, were arriving from all over the district by every hour by cab and by motor. Every car brought its load of men and women prepared for the worst, calm sad eyed wives and mothers. There were no outbursts of fevered hysterics, but there was many pathetic scenes. All who had relatives working at Chequerbent hurried to the colliery anxiously enquiring for tidings of their loved ones. Black faced workers were making their way homewards and as they came, they were claimed by rejoicing mothers and wives. One elderly miner was being led by the arms by his delighted spouse whose fears had been allayed. But, and today, the majority could learn nothing.

The pit bank was protected by a large force of the Bolton County Constabulary under Supt. Wilson and only those whose business took them within were admitted. The general public climbed onto the adjoining railway embankment anxious to get a view of the rescue work, but those who were merely curious could see nothing to satisfy morbid curiosity. Tools and big piles of ventilation brattice cloth were being taken into the mines by scores of willing helpers whilst intermittently the huge cage brought out the men who had been engaged in the Arley Mine.

A big staff of doctors were at the scene very quickly, but they had little to engage their attention, and it was feared that the ill-fated miners were beyond human aid. It was estimated that 352 men and boys were in the Yard Mine and an official stated that at noon he could not extend the faintest hope. The Lancashire and Cheshire Miner's Federation were represented, and practically every colliery in the district was represented by either its management or by gangs of helpers who are skilled in penetrating the awful secrets of the mines.

The unfortunate men had only entered the mine at a quarter to seven this morning, so that they had not been beneath the surface more than an hour when the accident occurred. The colliery is a comparatively new one and everything is on the most-up-to date principle. The Yard Mine, as far as I could ascertain, is 300 yds in depth and beneath it is the Arley Mine. I had a chat with a man who had just come to the surface from the Arley Mine. He said the shock was heard in parts of the workings beneath. There are four mines known as the Trencherbone, Yard, Arley and Quarter, and the Yard Mine is about midway between the Arley and the Trencherbone. There are two Winding Shafts known as the Uptake and the Down Shaft and it was in the former that the explosion demonstrated itself, and when this was put out of action, attention was concentrated upon the Down Shaft. The damage to be seen above the surface is comparatively slight. Some of the casing has been broken, and a quantity of brickwork has been damaged, but otherwise there is little to indicate the sad nature of the work proceeding below. Shortly after noon I was informed that all the men in the Arley Mine and Trencherbone mines were safe, but up to that time only four miners had been accounted for from the Yard Mine.

The joiner shop has been turned into an improvised mortuary and here the bodies are lying awaiting identification which, it is stated, will be a matter of considerable difficulty. The first effort at rescue was made without any delay by a number of colliers who were led by Mr Alfred Tonge, the Manager. They endeavoured to make their way into the Yard Mine, but before they had proceeded far they were met by overpowering fumes and had to beat retreat. Since then something like seventy men have grouped themselves into relief parties, and they have been directed by Sergeant Major Hill who is in change of the Howe Bridge Rescue Station. One of his lamp rooms was rapidly turned into a rescue station and here the bands fitted themselves with their equipment, and with their goggles they looked weird objects as they ranged around the pit-head prepared to make the descent.

One brave fellow who was a member of an early rescue party lost his life in his anxiety to help the entombed men. It has transpired that he was working without apparatus. A member of the party who was protected by his apparatus told our representative that the deceased was one of two men who were down in the Arley airway in between the Arley and the Yard mines. He was overpowered by gas, and it was recalled by his comrade that unless help was quickly forthcoming he would be beyond help. His comrades ran for assistance and then another member of the party with the oxygen apparatus was quickly upon the scene. He exhausted his supply of oxygen in trying to restore the brave fellow, but despite his efforts he was unable to bring him round and he succumbed before he could be brought to the pit shaft.

A member of the rescue party, during the morning, was successful in penetrating to the bottom of the Yard Shaft and it was stated that they could see the under-looker lying dead in his cabin whilst a number of other bodies were lying about, one of which was supposed to be the hooker-on whose corpse was terribly mangled.

A man came out with his head bandaged and he was a hooker-on at the bottom of the pit and he was at the foot of the Arley Shaft when the explosion occurred. He said he was blown between 12 - 14 yards and literally lifted off his feet. His head struck a tally-board and he was found in an unconscious condition, but he was restored to consciousness again shortly afterwards and got to the surface without difficulty. After receiving attention, he seemed little worse for his terrible experience.

Another incident which showed the terrible force of the explosion was the experience of a boy of Chequerbent. He was at the pit eye and was suddenly knocked over by the force and his leg broken . He was brought out of the mine, being one of the first to arrive at the surface from below. The approach to the pit is difficult and motor cars have to go a considerable distance through the fields and up several steep hills. The winding apparatus is in excellent order and the engine house and the engine are untouched.

Thursday, December 22nd 1910
COFFINS ARRIVE IN THE NIGHT
VIVID STORY OF WEIRD VIGIL
FEARED LOSS OF ALL THE ENTOMBED
MAYOR OPENS RELIEF FUND

The Christmas festivities in Bolton, Lancashire, indeed throughout the country are chastened by an appalling disaster in the No 3 Yard Mine at the Hulton Colliery Company (Pretoria Pits at Hulton). The full seriousness of the catastrophe is not yet known, but if the fears that are present entertained prove to be well-found, it will be the worst that has ever occurred in the Lancashire coalfields and will only be exceeded in the country's history by that of Oaks, near Barnsley in 1866. For some time almost eight hundred lives were in jeopardy and the fate of about 350 men and youths is still only a matter of conjecture. The feeling of those competent to express an opinion being that not one will escape with his life. Of the bodies recovered, only six have been identified.

The shafts of both mines are less than 80 yards apart, and the staging surrounding them is joined. A glance at the head gear of the Yard Mine soon showed that it was in that mine that the explosion had occurred, for some of the head gear was blown away falling on the roof of the Engine House some yards off, and the winding gear was disabled. This meant that the shaft was feared unsafe for the exploration purposes, and attention was directed to the adjoining one. There everything was found to be in working order. A fireman who was with the under manager in his office at the pit-eye when the explosion occurred told the Evening News Representative that the force of it was such as almost to throw them off their feet, and it was followed immediately by A RUSH OF FOUL AIR, which was so bad as to completely overcome some of the men and youths who had rushed from their working place into the main roads and were making with 'all speed' to the pit eye. The work of winding these men from the pit to the surface was immediately entered upon and before noon they had all been brought out.

Writing from the scene of the disaster at seven o'clock this morning, our representative says:-

The night has passed without bringing a single crumb of comfort to those who have kept a patient vigil at the pit. Since ten o'clock last night a little group of colliery officials, workmen, police officers and pressmen have stood around the pit shaft waiting for any scrap of information from the rescue parties who have descended and ascended the shaft at pretty regular intervals throughout the night, but the only news that has come from these sources has been of the most depressing and cheerless character. About eleven o'clock, a report was circulated on the surface that there was a bare possibility of some of the entombed men being rescued alive, and to give colour to these statements it was pointed out that one of the surface offices had been fitted up as a temporary hospital and that huge rolls of bandages had been sent down the pit in readiness for the treatment of the injured. Little 'hope' was attached to the report and any small hopes that the statements may have raised were dispelled on the return of the first party of rescue men with the information that large quantities of 'after-damp' were being encountered and that it was impossible for anyone to live in such a poisonous atmosphere. Deep gloom was written on every countenance when this announcement became general property, and the little party at the pit-head settled down again to their cheerless vigil still HOPING

AGAINST HOPE that the succeeding hours might bring some small rays of comfort.

With the break of dawn the scene became no more cheerful. Workmen flitted about the yard and when it became fairly light the scores of lamps which had been placed along the ground, marking out the dangerous spots to strangers, and on top of the steps leading to the pithead, were removed. Batches of men who were to take part in the work of exploration began to arrive from different collieries. These men reported themselves at the rescue stations and in due course got ready to go down the mine. A large batch of police had also arrived from the Bolton, Manchester, Wigan and Warrington divisions. There were forty in number and they took the places of the men who had had a weary watch throughout the night. Very little information could be obtained of what was going on underground, but it was reported that the work of the exploration was being thoroughly carried out to see if any men were likely to be alive.

It was reported at nine o'clock this morning, that there was not much probability of bodies being brought to the surface today, and also that there was little likelihood of any of the men or boys being found alive. No official statement however has been made and much anxiety was felt by the relatives with regard to the removal of the men who have already been found. "As I made my way from the tram car along the rugged field pathways to the colliery this morning," writes a member of our staff at the colliery, "a beautiful rainbow arched directly over the ill-fated shaft. One could not but wonder if that sign of 'Providence' had any meaning for those poor fellows lying hundreds of feet below the surface?" Did it mean that there was yet hope of having them from the foul air, in which we had awful evidence before that a number of their companions had

133

perished? Almost all hopes were dispelled very shortly after for that grim sign of death's visitation, the undertaker coffin-van, passed and brought back all the previous fears that nothing was left save hope. In the pit-yard there was an absence of hurry and bustle. The on-lookers were not as numerous, yet one saw a quiet orderly round of duties being pushed forward in the last hope of saving life. Those imprisoned miners, locked by cruel fate far down below, have been there almost 30 hours at the time I write and if there is still life, it must be a life of terrible anguish, yet we were not without the hope of life.

It was ascertained this afternoon that according to the check-weigh-man's book, 338 miners and two fitters descended the mine yesterday morning. Assuming that the entombed men are dead, and including the six bodies now lying in the mortuary and one at the infirmary, the death toll will be brought up to 347. (Our representative this afternoon asked if an official list of bodies could be furnished to the Press? It was stated that this was impossible, as all the names of the men are not in the books of the Company and in many cases, the miners had been working for contractors.)

"There is no hope, absolutely none - not the slightest shadow of hope at all of anybody being alive"

There were untold difficulties to be overcome below. A member of one of the rescue parties explained that there are five different roads branching off in all directions from the shaft from whence the work was preceding, and all were blocked. The explosion had brought down scores of tons of dirt from the roofs shattering timber like matchwood and throwing huge blocks of coal and rock in all directions. Before rescuers can proceed, these gigantic barriers have to be carefully removed and fresh timber fixed. The plucky fellows, who wear goggles and carry compressed oxygen cylinders on their shoulders, know no fear. They wait composedly upon the surface until the signal comes for them to take their turn below. At eleven-thirty, a gang of these grimy-faced heroes came out with dire news which, coming so shortly after Mr Gerrard's statement seemed a full confirmation of the worst fears. I asked their leader what had been their progress. "Oh we have made some progress. We managed to get to the coal face and there counted no fewer than forty-seven bodies on the east level. They lay there peaceful as though sleeping." I asked another miner about the ventilation and his reply was "As clear as a bell." The efforts of those who had been labouring to restore the ventilation had been effective and now the air was very good. "It's as clear as a bell," was how he picturesquely described its condition to me. The dirt has been practically all removed, you can form some idea of how comparatively clear the roads are now, which I can tell you that we have explored quite three hundred yards since six of clock this morning.

There was rather an ominous sign during the afternoon when two closed vehicles drove into the colliery and on enquiries being made our representative was informed that they contained a number of coffins for the reception of the remains. From the fact that an order had been given for one hundred and fifty coffins by a local firm, it was evident that there had not been much hope from the first. The coffins, which bore no identification plates and were of polished oak with brass mountings, were conveyed to one of the buildings in the colliery yard, adjoining the temporary mortuary.

The Mayor and Town Clerk of Bolton visited the colliery during the afternoon and the Mayor held an informal meeting in respect of his 'relief fund'.

A sixth body has been identified as a boy, sixteen years, of Leigh Road, Daisy Hill who was brought out of the workings yesterday afternoon. There is still one body, that of a boy, unidentified and during the morning over one hundred fear stricken people went to the mortuary to see it.

A secret consciousness that the splendid efforts which were being made to rescue the entombed men alive were destined to end in failure. Thus the last hour of the day that will have bitter memories for hundreds passed away. At midnight last, the watchers were still awaiting tidings of the progress of the rescue operations.

Overhead, the moon and stars shone splendidly from a cloudless sky, but one had to look up and away to note the peaceful beauty of the night, the immediate scene being brilliantly illuminated by a number of powerful lights suspended from various parts of the pit head.

Friday 23rd December
HULTON PIT CALAMITY
TODAY'S SCENES
CROWDS WAITING IN DEPRESSING WEATHER

The weather during the early morning was of a miserable character. The coffins were conveyed from the mortuary to the wagon-repairing shed. Sad scenes were witnessed at the two entrances which were guarded by police. A considerable number of people gathered around the door anxious to identify missing friends and relatives. The bodies now lying in the coffins in the shed are placed in a long line down one side of the building. On the lids are the bundles of clothing wrapped in white calico. It was a slow process and those waiting to pass through the mortuary appeared resigned to the fate of their relatives whom they had lost. Amongst the crowd were a number of people showing evidence of deep mental anguish.

There were many pathetic scenes outside the wagon shed and the Salvation Army men did much good in trying to comfort the grief stricken women who stood about.

One woman however, could not be consoled, despite the attention of the Salvationist who supported her and gave her cheery words. Her husband, it appeared, was an ex-army man and had only been home about three months. It was stated that he bore numerous tattoos marks, one of which, wailed the stricken wife, was on his arm and said. 'In memory of my dear mother'. "Let me go in," she urged, "I wish I could only speak to him once." "You must be brave and try to bear it," urged the officer. "I cannot bear it," she bitterly cried., "Its hard, oh it's hard!" She repeated her appeals to be allowed to go into the shed.

The whole place is pervaded with a sense of despair and desperation. The crowd on the pit bank is gradually increasing and though they see little or nothing of what is going on, they remain gazing steadily at the pit head, as if expecting that the great driving wheels over the two shafts were going to revolve and so bring back to the surface news of the progress being made in the bowels of the earth.

Passing along the incline leading to the pit this morning, one continually met with groups of weeping women who were slowly proceeding to the scene of the disaster. They were accompanied by children to the eminence overlooking the shaft. On one of the bridges near the winding place a large crowd gathered, their eyes being intently turned to the movements in the pit yard and also at the shaft. Whilst the people were coming up from the main yard, a large conveyance from Bolton drove up with a load of coffins. The writer was informed, however, by several men who were employed at the pit that it was improbable that any more bodies would be brought to the surface before this evening, although the rescue party were working diligently and evidently bringing the bodies to the bottom of the shaft ready for winding up to the top.

A large number of Atherton women have come forward to assist Miss Tonge in the work of preparing and supplying food to the hard-worked rescue bands and others, and also if necessary to help in the washing and laying out of the dead. Their offer has been accepted and arrangements have been made for them to be on duty at the colliery tomorrow.

The Rescue Worker's Plans (Official statement)

At 1.30pm this afternoon, Mr Gerrard made the following official statement:-

"The exploration of the Down Brow Yard district has been carried forward to the coal face and the far end has been visited. Some thirty-six bodies were located there. About the end of the road, the district was comparatively 'free from falls' so that the work of restoring the ventilation is very much facilitated. At this morning's conference of mining engineers it has been decided to reverse the ventilation so that the roads which were return roads will now be intake roads. This operation will probably take two hours and whilst it is proceeding the exploring party will be withdrawn. The exploring party will go forward to complete the examination of the Down Brow Yard, the North Plodder, the South Plodder and the South Yard. It is hoped that about fifty bodies will be brought out this evening."

Professor Redmayne, the well-known Home Office Expert, arrived shortly before 10 o'clock and joined the conference which had been going on for two hours in one of the colliery offices.

Stories in a nutshell

About a fortnight ago a young fellow of 22 who has no father, said to his mother, "You must give over working in the mill now, and I will keep you". What pathos.

A suggestion of maternal love and thoughtfulness was the finding of a red cheeked apple in the pocket of a dead lad.

Another case was that of an affectionate husband and father. It was his wont, when speaking of the uncertainty of his calling, to use what has proved a significant remark, viz. that "he hoped if ever he was killed in the mine, it would be with a lot, for then his wife and children would be looked after."

Two extraordinary cases came to light this morning, in the home of one family who have four members missing, one of them is a 13 year old boy and had only just left school. Wednesday, the fateful morning, was the first time he had gone to work. Another, was a youth who reached the age of 17 last Saturday and lived on Manchester Road, Chequerbent. He also went down the pit on Wednesday for what proved the first and last time.

THE DOOMED MINERS
BRINGING THE DEAD TO THE BANK
THROUGH THE NIGHT'S WATCHES
GRUESOME PROCESSION TO THE MORTUARY
THIRTY SIX BODIES REMOVED

If anything was wanted to make one realise the appalling tragedy of the disaster, it was provided by the steady procession of stretcher bearers with their ghastly burdens which commenced about 7.30 pm last night and continued to after midnight. The crowds of people who had gathered at the pit bank for the past two days had realised the utter hopelessness of further waiting and had almost all returned to their homes to weep out their sorrow. Only a band of press men and some colliery employees remained to watch the gruesome work of bringing the bodies of the unfortunate victims to the surface. Mr A G Tonge, the manager of the mine, who deserves the highest commendation for his untiring nay heroic energy, left the colliery about 10 o'clock last night and went home for a few hours rest. He was accompanied by Mr G Gerrard, the Mine's Inspector, and though this was the first time that either of them had gone off duty since the dreadful catastrophe occurred, they returned after an absence of about six hours.

The work of exploration had now been suspended and all that was to be done during the solemn hours of the night was to raise as many bodies as possible to the surface. A party equipped with breathing apparatus descended the Arley Mine and making their way through the Yard, entered the workings and commenced carrying the corpses from there to the pit mouth. There they were wrapped in cloth and sent to the surface up the Yard Mine shaft, one being placed on each deck of the only cage workable.

In what is known at the lower deck of the head-gear colliery office, members of the St John's Ambulance Brigade were waiting to remove the bodies and place them on stretchers. The ambulance men conveyed them to the joiner's shop mortuary. This was all the pressmen were able to see - except for brief glimpses into the buildings between the opening and closing of doors - but it is a sight that none of them will ever forget. Atmospherically the night was ideal though unreasonably mild, the sky being beautifully clear and the air almost balmy. Along the line taken by the melancholy procession of lifeless human forms, pit-lamps hung at intervals, emphasising the outer darkness and casting a sombre light along the road. At the head of each band of eight men with their two loaded stretchers walked a man with a lighted lamp. The scene was one of the most impressive in the history of this awful disaster and will live in the memory when the details have been crowded out.

Inside the temporary mortuary, the scene was one of gruesome activity. Dr T Boston Johnson of Manchester Road, Bolton, was in charge and he was assisted by a number of nursing sisters of the St. John's Ambulance Brigade. Some of these nursing sisters have done excellent service. One, who is an employee at the colliery, having been on duty ever since the explosion with an exception of about four hours yesterday afternoon. The bodies were taken from their wrappings and it was found that some of them were so mutilated as to be almost beyond recognition. They were badly charred and some had been stripped of clothing and the members severed by the force of the explosion. Some miners were scarcely damaged and had evidently been asphyxiated by the poisonous gases in the mine. They were stripped and washed and placed in coffins. The clothes from each body being placed on the coffin to assist in the identification of the victims. It was announced as soon as the bodies commenced coming to the surface that no-one would be admitted to the mortuary for identification purposes until today, but this regulation was relaxed during the night. At one o'clock this morning 30 dead bodies had been brought up, making 36 lying in the mortuary altogether, and operations were then suspended until 6 o'clock, the men underground devoting the intervening time to fixing props in the roads to render safer the task of those who should come after.

"Just let me touch him"

There was a most touching incident in the mortuary just after noon. The parents of a boy passed down the long row of coffins and the couple stopped at the coffin which contained the body of their boy. On the lid being raised the mother pleadingly said "Just let me touch him!" The mother affectingly placed her hand on his head and then burst into tears. The father also broke down and the scene was a most touching one, strong men biting their lips to hide their emotions. The mother was then assisted out of the shed by a supply of helpers. A sad fact in connection with that of the boy is that he was found by his father.

Inquest opened - Engine room as Coroner's court

The inquest was held in the engine room of the colliery this afternoon and the sight was an extraordinary one. The county Coroner, Mr S F Butcher, occupied a position in one corner of the room and witnesses and pressmen were huddled together as best they could, the only people with any degree of comfort being the jurymen. Amongst those present in the court were Professors Redmayne (Chief mining Inspector), Mr Gerrard (H M Inspector of Mines), Mr D J Shackle ton (Labour Advisor to the Home Office), Mr Brancker (Managing Director), Mr A J Tonge (Manager), Mr S Parker (Town Clerk at Bolton), Mr W T Wilson (MP for Westhoughton), Superintendent Wilson (Bolton Police), Mr Roughly (miner's agent), Mr T R Dotson (representing the local miners), Ald. Raffan (MP for Leigh Division), Councillor J Ashworth (JP, chairman, Leigh Liberal Association Executive) and many others.

The coroner remarked on the mournful circumstances in which they were assembled at this season of the year which presented itself to them as one of light, love and happiness, but they were face to face with a terrible tragedy and death and sorrow. The disaster into which they are called to enquire appeared likely to be fearfully enormous in its character and there was but slight hope that its enormity would be diminished. Still, they all hoped against hope. Everybody would sympathise with those bereaved, and also with the proprietors of the colliery. Funds would be forthcoming to relieve the needs of the sufferers and meanwhile it was the sad business of the jury to pay assiduous attention to the duties of that enquiry, and to try to discover anything which would assist in obviating such disasters. The Coroner proceeded to state that for the time being the interest of the jury would be restricted to the work of identification. They would have to meet every few days to enable those who were from time to time recovered to be identified and removed for burial. He invited the assistance of anyone who could throw any light upon the catastrophe to communicate with himself or with the Supt. of Police.

The Town Clerk of Bolton asked for the indulgence of the Coroner for a few minutes. As representing the Mayor and Corporation of Bolton, he desired to convey that Christmastide their feelings of great sorrow. He then announced the receipt of a telegram from the King at Buckingham Palace. Mr Parker also announced messages from His Grace the Archbishop of York, the Earl and Countess of Derby, The Lord Mayor of London, the Lord Provost of Glasgow, The Lord Mayor of Bradford, The Lord Mayor of Cardiff and many others. Mr Parker handed these in for observation of the Coroner and the Court. These made quite a large bundle and the sentiments "expressed very deeply" the condolence of the people in all parts of the Kingdom. Professor Redmayne, on behalf of Winston Churchill, expressed his sincere sympathy with the widows and orphans and also desired that "something might be elicited to render impossible any repetition of such dire calamity as these. Mr Branker also expressed the regret of the directors and other officials of the colliery at the much loss of the noble lives, and referred with much emotion to the poor fatherless children who had been left. He trusted something might be done to mitigate the sorrow and to discover the cause of the explosion which had been terrible. Mr Roughly, on behalf of the Miner's Federation, expressed both his deep grief and also his gratitude for the facilities rendered him and his colleagues by the colliery officials. Mr Dootson briefly added a few words on behalf of the relatives and the Coroner then began to call evidence.

The Evidence

The first case taken at the Inquest this afternoon in the engine house was that of a man of Church Street, Westhoughton, the Coroner remarking that the body was labelled No. 1. The deceased's son gave evidence of identification and said his father was a fireman at the colliery. He was in good health when he left home to go to work on Wednesday. The Coroner, "has he made any complaint of the conditions of his work?" Witness, "No sir."

These are five widows

Five women presented themselves at the door of the improvised mortuary and one of their number expressed a wish to view the bodies. With a catch in her voice she said "These are five widows." They were conducted by an officer to the wagon shed to go through the trying ordeal of viewing the bodies which had not been previously identified.

Work of the Rescue Party

About noon a party of rescue men from the Wigan Coal and Iron Company at Pretoria Pit, who had been down from 9.30am to 11.30am this morning, came to the surface and were interviewed by the Evening News representative before being driven off in a motor car to their homes. Although they had only come across three bodies they were able to report progress. "We have been in the Top Yard," stated one man, "and we have been able to get along without using the apparatus. We have been able to go a lot further than yesterday. The roads and air are good" He added that the three bodies were those of a fitter, a joiner and a labourer. They were badly burned and one of the men had a big stone on his head while another, who had a pinion wheel resting on his chest, had been knocked through a wall.

King and Queen Subscribe

A telegram was received this morning by the Mayor of Bolton to the following effect :-

I have it in command to announce to you that the King subscribes £500.00 and the Queen £100.00 to your fund for the relief of those dependents of the victims of the recent Hulton Mine disaster.

Their Majesties earnest prayer is that your prompt and kindly action, together with the universal sympathy that is so vastly shown, may to some extent be consolation to the poor widows and orphans whose hearts are wrung and whose homes are wrecked by the visitation of this dire calamity, Wm. Carrington, Buckingham Palace, London.

A sister's grief

The identification of a boy was attended by a distressing incident. A sister of the deceased who had accompanied her father was anxious to go into the temporary morgue, but the task of identification was left to the father. "If I could see my brother's belt I could tell if it was him," remarked the sister, who was peering through the strips of rough canvas which hung over the entrance roof of the shed. At this moment, the father was seen to lift the belt from the lid of the coffin. This

145

piece of leather was taken as evidence that the remains were of the young lad, and the sister fainted.

Probably not a single breast still harbours hope that living men will be found in the Yard Mine. The horrors revealed by the slowly passing hours, not less than the emphatic doom unanimously pronounced by the experts, have blotted out the last remaining rays of faith in the miraculous survival of those whom stunned relatives cannot yet think of as dead.

We must all turn sadly and sternly from leaning on dear desire. There are other things to do, other needs to serve, other hearts to cherish. All that can be done for the dead will be done by reverent and skilful hands, and equally every possible effort will be made to restore to their own habitations the mortal remains of those who died at duty's post. The vital spark, alas, is irrecoverable, but we of the wider community, however much we mourn for the dead, must labour well at mourning for the living. Their need is our debt. We are debtors all to the men who, whether through necessity or choice, take up the primary burden of providing this great country the wherewithal to build up its industrial greatness. Men who, with sinewy arms, bear our economic structure upon their bended back. Without her miners, Lancashire might have been a third-rate county in a third rate country, subordinate to other nations possessing other natural advantages over us. The South Lancashire coalfield has been one of the chief factors in the making of modern England and now is the time to remember it. Are there any flint-hearted enough at this hour to cavil at the miner's recklessness, his spendthrift nature, his domestic improvidence? Have they considered the nature of his toil, its exacting, arduous, monotonous nature? Thus in the winter months he sees little daylight and no sunshine from Sunday to Saturday? That every moment he is within an ace of death?

Truly, there is more excuse for him than for most when he passes from one extreme to another. But they know little of the mining community who construct a universal type from cases of imprudence or improvidence here and there.

It is simply not true that the miner is an ill-deserving victim of his own reckless folly. But if it were, not deserts, but needs must be the only guide to our generosity in this hour of terrible loss. The widows and orphans have to bear a loss which not all the gold of Croesus could assuage. They will bear it more bravely, with more heroic fortitude than most of us could summon in like circumstance, but in addition, while they fight down the grief within they have to withstand the hungry wolf at the door. We can a least keep him at bay or draw his sharpest teeth. Every part of the country is being applied to and from every corner of England practical help will come, but on this district must lie the chief care of the stricken homes and we therefore must earnestly ask that hearts may open pockets and support the appeal now before the public for an unstinted outpouring of aid in this dire hour. The twin of Grave needs is glorious opportunity.

The Wages

Amongst the strange sequels to the disaster, is the fact that the women today went for the last time for the pay-checks for the wages of the entombed husbands, brothers and sons. For today is pay day at Hulton Colliery Offices and wages are being paid out as usual.

Saturday 24th December 1910

TODAY'S SCENES
WHEN THE MORNING DAWNED
LINE OF COFFINED CORPSES

It was a weary scene on which daylight dawned at the colliery this morning. The wind sighed through the headgear as if mourning over this great calamity and the clouds intermittently wept silent tears of sympathy. Inside the mortuary the gruesome work of shrouding the dead was going on and the line of coffined corpses awaiting identification steadily grew. About nine o'clock horror-stricken and anguished relatives recommenced their terrible wait at the mortuary door. At nine-thirty the mine had disgorged about a third of its awful toll, and 107 wrecked human beings lay in a row. The Three-quarter district of the mine had been cleared and the 96 bodies which had been brought up since last evening had come from the Down Brow where about 150 are expected to be found on the east level. Several squads of men, 120 in all, had been at work carrying the human wreckage from the working places to the pit eye. They had undergone tremendous hardships having had to carry the bodies over rough heaps of fallen dirt in some places, but they had struggled bravely and heroically on until some of them had fallen from sheer exhaustion. One man had continued the tremendous task for over four hours and was brought to the surface suffering so acutely from the effects of the foul air and his hard toil that for some time his life was in danger and it was feared that he would become a victim of devotion and duty.

Preparing for burials

Several more of the corpses were removed to Chequerbent station later on last evening. A special van was utilized. The limbs of many of the bodies seemed to have sustained compound fractures, whilst other appeared to be burnt from the waist upwards, the writer was informed. The work of preparing the bodies for burial was carefully carried out and the mortuary presented a compelling spectacle, with rows of coffins, some of which were covered with purple cloth.

Special meeting of Westhoughton Council

A special meeting has been summoned for Monday evening to receive a report from the Chairman as to steps taken with respect of the relief fund.

Statement by Miner's Agent

Mr H Roughly, local miner's agent, desires us to give publicity to the following statement :- "As representative of the Lancashire and Cheshire Miner's Federation, and respectively of the miners in this district. I wish to give expression of my deep grief at this awful calamity. In the prosecution of my duties here during the last few days, I have seen and felt deeper sorrow than words can express. I think of wives, mothers and children whose bereavement is so terrible, and it seems a feeble thing to say that I sympathise deeply with them.

Yet I say from my heart, I want to thank very heartily that splendid band of helpers who have gathered around here – rescuers, doctors, officials and many others. I wish also to say that the managers of the mine have shown to me and other officials of my federation every possible courtesy, and have constantly proved their readiness to enter into consideration with us on all matters connected with the work of rescue. I can say with confidence that in our efforts to ameliorate the horrors of this catastrophe and to take advantage of every possible chance of saving life, all has been done that could be done. I deeply regret that our efforts in this direction have met with such small success."

THE RESUMED INQUEST
CORONER'S QUESTION TO EACH WITNESS

At 1 o'clock today, Mr S F Butcher resumed the inquest adjourned from yesterday, on those of the victims who had been identified since the last hearing. The engine house of the Yard Mine was again utilised as the Coroner's Court and, as was the case yesterday, one side of the long room was occupied by relatives and friends of the deceased workmen. There was a repetition of the distressing scenes which were witnessed in this quarter on Friday, many of the bereaved being unable to suppress their grief and, both before and during the inquiry, one heard the sound of women's sobs and the wailing cries of infants, some of whom were present with their mothers.

On the opposite side of the room to the relatives was the Coroner's table and the juror's seats, and close by these was seated Mr T R Dootson, the solicitor representing the Miner's Federation. At the outset of the inquiry the foremen gave expression to the juror's their sorrow at the disaster, and the Coroner then proceeded to take evidence of identification. Yesterday's plan of swearing in four of the relatives at once was repeated and the evidence, brief and formal was then tendered. In the case of each witness the Coroner made the inquiry, "Has he ever made any complaint about his work, so far as you know?" before evidence was taken.

Mr J Yearnshaw, foreman of the jury, rose and said he desired on their behalf to give expression to their feelings which were entirely in accord with the Coroner's remarks on Friday. They desired to join in the expression of sympathy to all the unfortunate sufferers in this disaster. They hoped, with the Coroner, that every assistance would be given during the course of the calamity and would be freely brought before them. By such a proceeding they were convinced they could only hope to discharge the duties that were allocated to them. Formal evidence was taken.

Bolton Mayor's Relief Fund

In the Mayor's dining room at the Town Hall last evening a representative meeting of citizens was held to take steps to inaugurate a relief fund. The Mayor said he did not think it necessary to say how sad was their meeting. They little thought a few days ago that, at this time of the year, they would have been faced with such a calamity that had fallen on the district. He expressed on their behalf to the widows and the children their deepest sympathy. That was all they could do so far, except that of taking the further step of doing something to relieve the suffering and distress to scores of families through having lost those upon whom they were dependent. He proposed the following resolution :-

This meeting, representative of Bolton and District, deeply deplores the day an awful calamity occurred at the Pretoria Colliery on Wednesday last, the 21st December, whereby a large number of men and boys lost their lives, and tenders to their relatives and dependants most heartfelt sympathy in the terrible bereavement they have sustained, and trust that divine strength and consolation will be vouchsafed in their hour of trial.

Mr P Westhead, Chairman of the Westhoughton Urban District Council, seconded. The experience he had passed through that day was one that would be impressed on his mind for a long time. He had served as one of the jurors, and the viewing of the bodies was an incident that no reasonable person would ever forget. He was sorry for the district of Westhoughton which had at this time of the year been plunged into such misery. It almost seemed that every family in Westhoughton was more or less effected by the catastrophe. He expressed his sincere thanks to the Mayor and those present for taking action to relieve the distress which was the result of the calamity. The resolution was put and carried unanimously.

Exact estimates are not yet possible but one gives one hundred and seventy as a number of widows, and another over a thousand of dependents. Besides the Compensation Act allowances - which cannot be granted immediately, and when granted are rightly administrated by weekly instalments - and the Miner's Permanent Relief Society - which has to act within certain strict rules - a more elastic fund of a substantial sum is required to meet elementary needs. In the Maypole Disaster, involving some seventy lives it was found that £15,000 was necessary under this particular head, and assuming similar needs at Hulton, £50,000 will be required. This in fact is the sum named by the Mayor of Bolton.

Mr Miles Burrows, one of the proprietors of collieries adjacent to the Pretoria Pit, and a gentleman thoroughly acquainted with the industrial and social conditions of the district, expressed the opinion at last night's meeting that £100,000 should be aimed at. It is evident that the Keeper of the King's Privy Purse, who is in a unique position in regard to relief funds, considers that a very large sum will be required, for His Majesty's subscription of £500.00 is a relatively large one, and, together with the Queen's and Queen Mother's gifts will, we are sure, greatly encourage our Mayor in the very generous task he has undertaken. The example set by the King and other distinguished contributors is, in effect, an urgent call to all classes to give accordingly to their ability.

Many of the contributions to our own fund are from the humblest workers, to whom the giving up of a shilling is a real sacrifice: even gold has come to our office counter from individual artisans, stirred into abounding generosity by a deep sense of brotherhood with their fellows whose last thoughts would be of widows and bairns left in need of bread. We most heartily thank all those who have responded nobly and quickly. We appeal again on Christmas Eve, that in every home, round every festive board, there shall be practical expression of sympathy with those whose gaze and thoughts will be fixed not on holly or mistletoe, not on steaming fare, not on blithe-hearted children's games, but on the coffin upstairs or the unrecovered mortality of loved ones in the dark tomb of the mine.

Contributions First, Inquiry After

Rumour is very busy all over the district, and in particularly Westhoughton, circulating statements - some of which have reached us - alleged to have been made by men working at the pit as to their fears and apprehension of possible disaster. It is obviously unwise to give comment on such reports and so distract attention from the immensely important duty at the moment, that of practical sympathy by contributions to the fund for the sufferers of the calamity. In due time, the fullest inquiry will take place and any fact as to the experience of workmen in the pit during the day immediately preceding the explosion will, as a matter of course, come before the coroner.

Westhoughton's Increasing Sorrow

Every hour confirms the truth of the statement that the township of Westhoughton suffers the most by the calamity. The Vicar of Westhoughton informs our representative that Chequerbent seems to have been hit the most, having informed him that one hundred families are affected in the part of the township of Chequerbent, whilst in the parish of St Bartholomew's. There are between sixty and seventy families bereaved, fifty at Wingates, and about forty at Daisy Hill.

Three Out of Fifteen Football Players Left

The Church of the Sacred Heart has been made poorer by the loss of many of its members. Out of a team of fifteen youths in the Sacred Heart Football Club only three are left.

Local Sportsmen Lost

Many notable characters in local sport are amongst the list of the lost. Footballers, cricketers, bowlers and harriers are amongst the fallen

Hatless Widow With Her Baby

A poorly dressed woman wearing a shawl and hatless, walked up to a policeman stationed near the pit head. She was carrying a baby and her enquiries were for her husband. Her visit availed nothing and she retraced her steps to the station.

An Old Hero and Mining Cards

On a miry roadway leading from the Bolton and Atherton tram route to the Pretoria Pit are one of two beggars. One of these is a man without a limb, and though there is no visible suggestion that he is a maimed collier, he is obviously present with a view to gaining the sympathy of those passing.

A more interesting figure is a veteran of the mine who has an illuminated address regarding how Dr John Dunbar displayed bravery in the Pendlebury Disaster twenty five years ago. He says that, now being out of work, he wants to earn a living and is now selling Memorial Cards of the old fashioned type bearing the following.

In loving memory of the Unfortunate miners

Who lost their lives in the terrible explosion at

Pretoria Colliery on December 21st 1910

In health and strength we left our homes
Not thinking death so near
It pleased the lord to bid us come
And in his presence to appear
When we arose in the early morning
Full of health, so blithe and gay
We little thought it was the dawning
Of our last and dying day.

In the midst of life we are in death

Tuesday 27th December

Reporter's remarks of Monday's gathering (Boxing Day 1910)

Visitors numbering thousands from the surrounding districts again flocked to the colliery all day on Monday. In the afternoon the cars were insufficient to cope with the surging passes of people, many of whom had travelled from Manchester, Oldham and Lancashire centres. The heavy driving rain simply drenched the crowds. As was the case on each of the preceding days, all save those who had business at the pit are rigorously excluded from the immediate precinct of the ill-fated mine. Large numbers, however, again secured a vantage point on the embankment from which they were able to obtain a distant view of the mournful procession of stretchers bearing bodies from the Yard Mine shaft to the mortuary, and the dispatch of coffined victims who had been identified at the Coroner's court to the hearses in waiting or the train which was in readiness to convey them to Chequerbent Station. The vicinity of the mortuary was besieged with a crowd of bereaved relatives waiting to identify the dead, and in groups of two's and three's they were conducted within the death chamber and allowed to look at the occupants of the coffins and at the bundles of clothing and other belongings of the deceased.

Many of the bodies which have been raised during the last twenty four hours however, are in an advanced state of decomposition, and it was deemed as feasible to photograph the remains in several cases and then seal the coffins. The scenes within the mortuary were too gruesome to permit detailed description. Policemen and ambulance men moved about the interior with handkerchiefs pressed to their mouths, and some of the relatives who came forward to identify the remains were overcome by sickness and had to be led away and succoured by ambulance men. The identifications proceeded steadily all day and every half hour or so, more bodies were raised by the Yard Mine shaft and conveyed to the mortuary. The Coroner's inquest was resumed at half past ten, and the court sat continuously until four o'clock with an adjournment which was taken at six o'clock. Up to the adjournment, evidence of identification of 209 victims had taken. When the court rose in the evening, 120 identifications had been taken during the day. It was stated that, up to that time, 253 bodies had been recovered from the mine, 26 of these having been raised to the surface on that day. Forty-two bodies were lying in the mortuary awaiting identification.

Christmas in Bolton

Christmastide in Bolton had a dark shadow cast upon it by the disaster at Pretoria Colliery, and the festive season was robbed of much of its brightness. The weather on Christmas Day was fine and in the early morning carols were sung and bands played. At the services in the churches and chapels music suitable to the season was sung and the preachers made

156

touching reference to the gloom which had been cast over the district by the colliery disaster.

At several churches, collections were taken on behalf of the disaster fund opened by the Mayor. On Monday, the mills and workshops were closed. The streets were crowded with pleasure seekers during the day. In the afternoon, rain fell heavily and the houses of entertainment were crowded. Thousands of people went out to 'Hulton' in the afternoon by the tramcars to view the scene of the explosion.

PIT CALAMITY
THE CORONER'S INVESTIGATIONS
SERIOUS ALLEGATIONS
RESUMING THE INQUEST

On the way to the colliery, I (the reporter) got in conversation with a collier, one of that large and brave band of men who have heroically faced perils to bring out of the mine their dead comrades and restore them to their sorrowing relatives. He was hurrying to his work at the pit but of his experience below ground he would not say much. " It is something awful," he remarked "what I have seen. I came across a group of ten men. Some of them had been knocked about, but more of them had just fallen asleep. One poor fellow had his breakfast can between his legs and another had his handkerchief close to his face. Some of them were bonny chaps, I can tell you. It was awful, but it is a good job they died in their sleep."

For a time on Christmas Day the colliery was bathed in sunshine, but it was a sad scene upon which the radiant rays fell. In the early hours, especially, there was a stillness about the colliery that was most impressive and in the yard were small groups of people who had come to view the dead in the hope of finding their missing relatives. In the temporary

157

morgue were many affecting scenes. It was difficult to realise that the scores of coffins which were laid side by side in the building contained the remains of some poor fellows or youths who a few days previously had been hearty and strong and together below ground. Scores of women and men had passed through the mortuary, and a large number of bodies were identified during the day. The police and ambulance men on duty had a most trying task. The gases given off by the decomposing bodies made the air of the mortuary noisome and disinfectants had to be freely used. The workers, however, nobly did their duty and reverently paid tribute to the dead by gently removing the coffin lids so that a view might be obtained of the remains by the relative. There were so many sobs and wails from the widows as they identified their loved ones. Some of them were led blindly out of the place, so great their grief, and it was in these cases that the Salvation Army women, who have been in attendance every day from the time of the explosion, could minister words of sisterly comfort.

The viewing of bodies went on till dusk, and many bundles of clothing which were tied up and placed on the coffins indicated that in these cases identification had been established. Three bodies of youths brought up on the first and second days had not been identified, so charred were the remains. In these cases measurements were taken of the bodies as a probable means of establishing their identity.

In the afternoon, thousands of people proceeded to the colliery. On the railway embankment to the left of the Arley mine they stood in long lines for several hours. It was a silent crowd and the police had no difficulty in keeping them outside the cordon which had been drawn round the colliery workings. Having spent some time in gazing at the colliery, the curious ones left the embankment and their places were quickly taken by others who had been attracted to the spot.

Resuming the inquest in the engine room at the pit this morning, Mr Butcher briefly opened the proceedings by stating they would first deal with a number of the bodies unidentified, and yet which must be buried. He would also deal today with all the bodies identified since his last sitting.

Details of Bodies Not Identified.

(Note to the reader: the description of unidentified bodies were posted in the Bolton Evening News so as to help families with identification of family members. The author has picked at random.)

Body No 9. And having no tally number, age apparently about 14 years. Height 4ft 10in, spare in arms and limbs, small hands and thin fingers, ears well set back. Remains are so burnt as to be beyond recognition. There is no clothing.

Body No 12. Tally number 865, age apparently 14 years. Height 4ft 9in. Spare build, disembowelled, top of head blown off, thin arms, fairly good legs. Clothing : grey tweed trousers with patch of calico on right hand at top, odd metal button, one leather grey garter, tanned light and not much worn.

Body number 42. Tally number 892, aged about 15 years. Height 5ft 9 in. Medium build, fairly well nourished. Disemboweled, legs much torn. Unrecognisable. Hair burnt off.

Body number 136. Tally number 1011. Age about 45 years. Height 5ft 10 in. Black or dark brown hair, with moustache. Two old cut-marks down centre of forehead. Full, round face.

Clothing : clogs size 9, soles filled with leather - narrow white cotton tape for laces, pit drawers white - several patches on left leg. Belt 1in. leather, steel buckle unstitched and held together with twine: Stockings: crown wool mixture, darned at the heels and foot with black wool.

Body number 225. Tally number 1063. Age about 30 years. Height 5ft 10in. Stout build, dark brown hair. Head in a 'pulp', unrecognisable (no photo). Clogs size 9, three lace holes, round toes, leather laces decorated front - embroidered leather. Belt 1in. leather, brown buckle and fastened with two brass studs. Socks: green wool. Trousers: black cord, much patched with similar material.

In the history of Lancashire Coal Mining Industry, Christmas Day of 1910 will be one of the saddest, for the thoughts of thousands were centred on Pretoria Pit, the scene of the great disaster, and hundreds of widows and children who have been robbed of their bread winners. Thousands of people visited the neighbourhood of the mine. "Journeying from Bolton to Atherton," writes one of our representatives who spent Christmas Day at the pit "I met a sad procession near Four Lane Ends, consisting of two hearses and a coffin carriage. These were conveying to their late home (a father and two sons)."

Official Statement This Afternoon

Mr A J Tonge and Mr Walker this afternoon made the following statement to an "Evening News Representative" as a result of their several hour's investigations below ground, starting this morning:- The managers, inspectors and engineers have been down the pit head again during the night. The progress was not quite as satisfactory as we could have wished. We went into the North Plodder and made arrangements for the clearing out afterdamp a little more quickly if possible. What we have been down for is to consider whether to return the ventilation to its original direction and after consultation down below it was decided to proceed as we have been doing with the ventilation reversed as it has been for the past few days. Parties have now gone down to again endeavour to get round the coal face and we hope to be able to do that by tonight. No more bodies can be recovered until that work is done. In the Top Yard section we are doing similar work with the same end. We have not seen any bodies today, but there is no doubt that some bodies remain to be found in the falls. The whole of the mine has now been explored. There will then be very little further news this afternoon and only after sundown will the bringing up of bodies be renewed. Crowds of people are visiting the region of the pit, bicycles and motors conveying numerous would-be observers of the proceedings, but they cannot ever get within view of the rescue parties as they traverse the short length of road from the sheds to the pit heads.

4.30pm

One of the explorers has just returned from the air crossing of the Top Yard and reports that Mr Gerrard and his party have gone forward to explore. This means that the party is making headway towards the coal face as hoped for in the interview reported earlier.

Homes for the Orphans (Gen. Booth's Offer)

The following telegram has been received from General Booth: To the Mayor of Manchester. In the distressing circumstances which so many of your suffering people find themselves, can I help by placing fifty orphans in suitable homes? If so, let me know - General Booth, Salvation Army, London.

Wednesday 28th December

The scene at the Pretoria Pits this morning was decidedly wintry, a thick hoar frost covering the equipment and surrounding country. A slight fog overhung the district. Throughout the night, the workers underground had directed their energies to fighting gas. One explained to an Evening News Representative this morning that they had made very little headway since Sunday until Tuesday night, and he described the gas as the hardest to move that he have ever come across. During the night, however, they had been rearranging the bratticing and the results had been very satisfactory, considerable progress having been made and the work would now be able to proceed with greater safety. The number of bodies recovered was added to during the night to the extent of nine making 272 brought to the surface in all.

Mr Gerrard, H M Inspector of Mines, told Press Representatives in the early hours of the morning "that all the work now remaining to be done was in the North Plodder and Top Yard Mines, and he was greatly disappointed that they had not been able to recover all the bodies by now. The difficulty they were experiencing was to get enough air forward into the workings to dispose of the afterdamp. There was nothing wrong with the fans but falls of roof were covering the air current to short circuit it, and they had often to retrace their steps to where the short circuit had occurred to fix brattice cloth to prevent it. In this way they had frequently lost two or three hours, but they could not go on removing bodies until this work was done. They were proceeding with the greatest caution so as to avoid the loss of further life. A rescue team was still accompanying all working parties as a precaution which very greatly minimised the risk. He paid a compliment to the splendid work of the rescue men. Of the nine bodies brought up to the surface this morning, three were boys. Three came from the Top Yard section and six came from the North Plodder. It is not likely that any more will be brought up before nightfall, but the workers expect to have all out tomorrow night except those buried under the falls. After that, they will only be recovered with great difficulty and the work will of necessity be very tedious.

There are now only 24 bodies left in the mortuary. One of the bodies brought up during the night is said to be unrecognisable, but it may be identified by other means. A police officer told our representative that two or three people went to the pit with copies of the "Evening News" in their hands to claim bodies which are there described.

More Description of Bodies

Body Number 250. Tally number 1159. A male person about 26 years old, round features. 5ft 9in. Good teeth in upper jaw, none in lower. Pair of clogs, three lace holes, size 9's with leather laces, squared toed, steel toe caps, and newly-ironed thin rope apparently used as a belt, heather mixture woollen ribbed stockings, far worn, light calico pit drawers, no buttons.

Thirteen Unidentified in One Grave

Westhoughton has been sadly hit by the disaster. The greater portion of the male workers are colliers, and no fewer than 239 of them have been killed in the explosion. The township therefore is the principal centre of mourning, and today a pall of gloom seemed to hang over the place (writes our representative). There have been a large number of funerals since Sunday (Christmas Day) and there was again a long list today. The scene was a dismal one and from 10 o'clock this morning there has been a procession of funeral parties visiting the cemetery close by the Parish Church.

PM : The weather was bitterly cold. The scene at the cemetery also had a chilling effect for in every portion piles of upturned clay was the sight presented. The streets bore a sombre appearance, pedestrians moving quietly about whilst conversations were carried on in subdued tones. Blinds were drawn throughout the district. The remark made to our representative accurately sums up the feeling in the town - "I've never heard anyone wish anyone a Merry Christmas." As for grave diggers this morning, there was about fifty men pursuing this task. One of the outstanding features was the interment of thirteen unidentified bodies in a large vault, specially prepared. Its size was 16 foot by 7 foot. The coffins were then covered with earth, but a portion of the vault was left unfilled, prior to the arrival of five more of the unclaimed dead which were expected to arrive from the pit during the day.

Amongst the bodies interred were those of four boys, apparently about fourteen years old. There is some talk of a public subscription list being opened to erect a monument over the vault.

About noon, there was a slight fall of snow, but later this gave way to drizzling rain. In the afternoon, the sad scene became intensified when four brothers were buried. There was a large crowd of on-lookers and the scene when the coffins were carried on the shoulders of the bearers from the church to the graveside was deeply touching. Women with shawls over their heads lined the pathway and there was many a tear-filled eye, whilst the men stood with heads bowed and uncovered as the long procession of grief stricken mourners passed by. The vicar read the committal lines as each body was lowered into the grave, and many a human form was shaken with anguish as the mind reverted to an attempt at picturing the home so rudely broken up by the loss of its young manhood. The test was a severe one for those befell. After the coffins had been lowered, the crowd quietly gathered round the graveside, and reverently dropped pieces of earth on the lids of the coffins as they took a last long look.

More pathetic scenes were witnessed in Westhoughton, when over 50 of the victims were interred in the Westhoughton Cemetery and the churchyards in the township. The day was fine but cold, a keen frost prevailing throughout the day. Nevertheless, the weather conditions were more favourable than on the preceding day. The streets and the churchyards were crowded with on-lookers and signs of grief were on every hand. Several persons fainted at Westhoughton Church and at Wingates Church. As the mourners of the last round of funerals were leaving the church, two of the women swooned when walking down the aisle. They were assisted by men wearing regalia of friendly societies who happened to be in reach.

Gravediggers Working Night and Day

The funeral parties come and go through the streets with a regularity which is appalling. The body in the hearse would be followed by mourners on foot, in some cases one carriage being requisitioned. The funeral parties were not such as one sees in big towns: silk hats were conspicuous by their absence and the mourners, generally speaking, wore the ordinary Sunday black of the collier. At the cemetery the repetition of the words "I am the resurrection and the life" by the four officiating clergymen became monotonous. While the services were being conducted, about forty diggers were preparing the other graves for the reception of the bodies. Indeed the grave diggers are working night and day.

Westhoughton Miners and Their Dead Comrades

A meeting of the miners employed at the Westhoughton Coal and Canal Company pits was held in the club-room of the Commercial Hotel in Church Street on Tuesday evening when the following resolutions was unanimously passed:- "That the Westhoughton branch of the Lancashire and Cheshire Miner's Federation deeply deplores the sad and awful calamity which has befallen upon the district by the explosion at Pretoria Pit of the Hulton Colliery Company at Westhoughton on Wednesday December 21st 1910, whereby a large number of our fellow workmen and boys have lost their lives, and hereby tenders to the widows and dependants and relatives of the victims most heartfelt sympathy in the terrible bereavement they have sustained, and trusts that divine strength and consolation will be vouchsafed and temporal help forthcoming in this, their hour of trial.

It was decided to grant £20.00 to those men who would be unemployed through the calamity and it was left with the committee to see what other funds were formed so that they could join them for that purpose.

THE GREAT DISASTER
"BOLTON EVENING NEWS" SHILLING FUND

THE MAYOR OF BOLTON (ALD. J.T. COOPER J.P) HAS OPENED A FUND FOR THE RELIEF OF THE WIVES AND FAMILIES OF THE VICTIMS OF THE HULTON COLLIERY DISASTER.

IN MAKING KNOWN THE NEEDS OF THE SUFFERERS, AND IN COLLECTING SUBSCRIPTIONS, THE ASSISTANCE OF THE PRESS OF GREAT BRITAIN HAS BEEN SOLICITED, AND AN APPEAL HAS BEEN ESPECIALLY MADE TO US TO GIVE SUCH HELP AS

THE GENEROSITY OF OUR READERS ENABLES US TO GIVE. WE HAVE THEREFORE OPENED A SHILLING FUND AS AN AUXILIARY TO THE MAYOR'S FUND, AND WE EARNESTLY ENTREAT OUR READERS TO MAKE AS PROMPT AND GENEROUS A RESPONSE AS THEIR CIRCUSTANCES PERMIT IN AID OF THE VICTIMS OF THIS UNPARALLELED DISASTER. VOLUNTARY WORKERS THROUGHTOUT THE TOWN ARE KINDLY GIVING THEIR SERVICES IN COLLECTING FOR THE FUND AND WHAT INCIDENTAL EXPENSES THERE MAY BE WILL BE DEFRAYED BY OURSELVES, SO THAT EVERY PENNY SUBSCRIBED WILL GO DIRECT TO THE MAYOR OF BOLTON WITHOUT DEDUCTION OF ANY KIND. SUBSCRIPTIONS OF ONE SHILLING AND UPWARDS SENT TO THE SECRETARY, "EVENING NEWS" OFFICE, MEALHOUSE LANE, BOLTON, WILL BE ACKNOWLEDGED IN THE PAPER.

Mainstay of Father and Mother
A woman had to be accompanied with a seat whilst she told the jury that the body of number 225 was that of her son who had made complaint about his work. The Coroner, "Has he lived with you?" "Yes, he was the mainstay of his father and me."
Air Hot
A man having said that body number 254 was that of his son added that the latter had complained of the conditions of his work. "What has he said?" "He said it was very hot air and the lamps were hot."
The wife of a miner said her husband had complained of gas in the mine and said if he continued working in the same place for

another week he would have been in it and would have had to come back home.

A Sad Christmas Birthday

The father of a boy from Brancker Street said his son would have been seventeen on Christmas day.

Thursday 29th December 1910
REVELATIONS OF THE MINE
EXPLORING THE NORTH PLODDER SECTION
THEORY THAT SOME MEN LIVED 24 HOURS AFTER THE EXPLOSION

So far as the recovery of bodies from the Pretoria Pit is concerned, Wednesday 28th was the day of least progress since the awful catastrophe occurred. For almost 24 hours the services of the stretcher bearers were not needed at all, viz. from about four o'clock on Wednesday morning till two o'clock this morning, and then only two lifeless forms of men were raised. It was stated that there are other bodies at the pit eye and they may be brought to the surface today. Those raised during the night have come from the North Plodder section and they are in a better state of preservation than those brought up recently. They show indications of the men having died from a natural death, and the theory has been formed that they lived for a day or possibly more after the explosion in the pure air behind a fall. This indicates that had rescuers been able to get into the workings within the first twenty four hours after the explosion, some of the poor miners might have been rescued alive.

This morning the rescue and exploring parties descended by the Yard Mine Shaft, which has only been used for bringing bodies previously. It is understood that repairs are being carried out in the Arley shaft. The anxiety of the people to get

168

their dead into their own possession is demonstrated by the fact that only five coffins remained in the mortuary this morning, one of them contains body number 112 which has been out of the mine since last Friday. The police have had the burial order for two days and have twice contemplated sending it away for interment with the unidentified, but each time someone has turned up who thought they recognised the remains and they have been held back. One woman thought the body was that of her husband. The body is gassed and the features swollen, but she thought she recognised a piece of harness which was used as a belt and a dog collar which served for a garter. About noon the woman came to the colliery again with her four sons who verified her impression that the body was that of her husband. This left only two bodies in the mortuary unidentified.

Statement by General Manager

About ten o'clock this morning Mr Alfred Tonge, the indefatigable manager of this and the Company's other pits, made the following statement to the Evening News Representative:- "We are just getting on as well as we can with the ventilation, but the falls have been holding it back. It seems to be more clear inside now, and we hope to have a very good day in the North Plodder. We have seen about twenty bodies there and about six in the Top Yard, and there are bodies that are exposed, leaving between twenty-five and thirty under falls of roof.

Asked how long it would take to get the bodies from under the falls, Mr Tonge said it might be a fortnight before the pit was got clear of bodies.

Miner's Premonition of Death

One of the many unfortunate miners who resided in the neighbourhood of Seddon Street, Westhoughton, and whose body had up to Wednesday night not been discovered, made a remarkable statement to his wife the night before the accident. She was engaged in patching his pit trousers, putting two brown patches on the knee and a white one at the back. Her husband commented upon the contrast between the white patch and the dirty cloth. "Never mind," she said "your coat will cover it up and it will soon get dirty in the pit." "No doubt," he said and then added " it'll do to identify me." It would almost appear that this miner had a premonition of something about to happen.

Mayor's Fund Over £20,000

One of the rooms at the Town Hall presents a remarkable and most interesting sight. Significantly the widespread sympathy there is for those bereaved. A special staff of nearly twenty is on duty carefully going through letters with cheques, postal orders, bank notes and other remittances and, incidentally, it may be said that fifteen clerical workers were on duty throughout the holidays to prevent any accumulation of messages or delay in sending receipts.

Ex Collier Offers to Adopt a Child.

Amongst the letters that reach the Bolton Town Hall are some truly of practical sympathy . A letter enclosed states :- I have been a miner sixteen years but it is close upon five years since I left that. I am now a dairyman. I have only one child, a boy of eight, and me and my wife would like to adopt a healthy girl from four years upwards. If you know of any that has been destitute it would have a good home and be brought up respectably in every way, and will have no bad habits shown to it. We want it entirely as our own and it would be treated as such.

Acknowledgements

A special thanks goes out to: my husband and best friend Nigel and my wonderful son, Alex, who I adore. Without their help and support I would not have achieved my goal. I love you so much.

To my Mum and Dad for being who you are and for making me who I am. My Aunt, Mary Berry, for help, support and encouragement whilst writing this book and for organizing me. Thank you

Brian Claire, Councilor, from Westhoughton, who has given me a wealth of information regarding Pretoria, David Smith (Author) for advice and for the loan of two postcard photographs included in this book. Ian Savage, Editor in Chief - Bolton News and the team for allowing me to use the wonderful words of a reporter in 1910 – Thank You for your kind permission.

With special thanks to Westhoughton and Bolton Library for their help, support and encouragement and for the use of the photograph of Brancker Street photo.

Special thanks go out to my cousin, Susan Hoy (nee Gore) and my wonderful family in Pennsylvania, USA for help and information, and to all my friends too numerous to mention, you know who you are, thank you for your support.

To my Ancestors who I have loved and lost, especially my Great Great Grandmother, Elizabeth Gore, upon whom this book is based.

To my publishers, Peakpublish and the directors, Geraldine & Sridhar, for all their work and guidance, support, and patience during the publication process.

If you found this book interesting you may enjoy reading
'From Coaldust to Stardust' by Jackie Toaduff
ISBN: 978-1-907219-08-5
A true story of a boy working for 13 years as a coal miner
in County Durham whilst clog dancing every chance he
could. He became the British Clog Dancing Champion,
made 17 solo appearances at the Royal Albert Hall and
danced with the likes of Princess Margaret and Ginger
Rogers.

*"**Billy Elliot pales in comparison.** It is the ultimate feel-
good, rags to riches story."*
Rick McKay, Broadway Producer/Director

*"My father danced on a table top, a chair, a piano, a bar
top but he never danced on a barrel. How I wish he could
have seen Jackie Toaduff do so and on a moving ship.
Daddy would have loved it."*
*Ava Astaire McKenzie, **Daughter of Fred Astaire***

*"**From coal miner to headliner**, he has enchanted and
fascinated all those with whom he would share the story
of his life."*
Margaret Obrien, Academy Award Winning Actress